ON THEIR WAY TO LIVERPOOL STREET STATION

the grand tier, the fram
with panels of rainbow ti
by bouquets, from which
more tasteful scheme c
stalls and boxes were fil
tlemen in Court dress
arrival of the Royal par
"God Save the Queen" was grand in the extreme. Rarely, too, has a more notable assemblage appeared in a Royal box at the opera-house, even at a State representation. Of our English Royal family there was, of course, a very strong contingent, including the Prince and Princess of Wales and their unmarried daughters, the Duke and Duchess of Edinburgh, the Duke and Duchess of Connaught, the Duke and Duchess of Teck, and many others. The change in the arrangements also permitted the appearance at the performance thus held in their honour of the Duke of York and the Princess May, whose reception, it need hardly be said, was of the most enthusiastic character. Amongst the foreign notabilities present were the King and Queen of Denmark, grandparents of the bridegroom; and the Cesarewitch. It was a pleasing innovation, suggested by Sir Augustus Harris and accepted by the Prince of Wales, for once to abandon the scheme usual on State occasions of a *spectacle coupé*, or a series of detached scenes from various favourite operas. Both from the point of view of art and effect the *spectacle coupé* has always been a failure, and although, perhaps, the new departure may not be popular with the artists of the Royal Italian Opera, many of whom were thereby excluded from the representation altogether, it was in every way preferable that the programme should be confined to one opera. The work chosen was M. Gounod's *Roméo et Juliette*, sung in French, with Madame Melba as the heroine, M. Edouard de Reszké as Friar Lawrence, M. Jean de Reszké as Romeo, and otherwise a familiar cast. The Polish tenor had, during the previous week, been confined to his room by a sprained ankle; but—as he pleasantly suggested, when assuring the manager that, well or ill, he would appear on the stage at the State function—there would have been nothing extraordinary even if Romeo limped a little, considering that he was so strongly addicted to the climbing of balconies.

The Arrival of the Distinguished Guests

A NUMBER of very distinguished personages, for the most part the near relatives of the bridegroom, began to arrive in London a few days before the wedding. On June 30 the King and Queen of Denmark, who are Prince George's grandfather and grandmother, reached Harwich on board the Royal yacht *Dannebrog*, escorted by a Danish man-of-war, and saluted on arrival by a Royal salute from the forts and H.M.S. *Mersey*. Prince Waldemar accompanied them. They were received by Lord Acton on behalf of the Queen; by General Ellis representing the Prince of Wales, and by the Danish Minister and Consul. At St. Pancras their Majesties were met by the Prince and Princess of Wales, the Duke and Duchess of Edinburgh and their families, the Duke of Cambridge, and the Duke and Duchess of Teck. About the same time in the morning the Czarewitch arrived at Flushing on board the Royal yacht *Victoria and Albert*. He was received by Admiral Sir A. Heneage, Commander-in-Chief at the Nore, and by a Guard of Honour of 100 bluejackets, while a Royal salute was fired by H.M.S. *Thunderer*. The Prince and Princess of Wales, the Dukes of Edinburgh, York, and Cambridge, and the Russian Ambassador met the Czarewitch at Charing Cross, and accompanied him to Marlborough House, where he has been staying for the wedding. The Grand Duke of Hesse, the son of the late Princess Alice, came to England to attend the marriage of his cousin, and went down to Windsor as the guest

bouquet from the Duke of York. About seven o'clock the Princess and the Duke and Duchess of Teck drove to Marlborough House to join the Prince of Wales's Dinner-Party, at which the King and Queen of Denmark and all the members of the Royal Family in London were present. After dinner the Royal party paid a State visit to the Covent Garden Opera-House.

The State Performance at the Opera

It was a happy idea of the Prince of Wales to fix the night of the State performance at the Opera for Tuesday, instead of on the evening of the Royal marriage, when, as vehicular traffic was prohibited in the streets, it would have been impossible for the company to reach the opera-house at all. No doubt this sudden change imposed considerable trouble on Sir Augustus Harris and his staff, but the energetic impresario at once set to work, and between midnight on Monday and six P.M. on Tuesday the opera-house was transformed from its ordinarily somewhat dingy appearance into a veritable marriage boudoir. White, of course, was the predominating colour, but plenty of relief was afforded by festoons of flowers, which formed a considerable feature of the decorations. Ropes of flowers were gathered up at the box-partitions by wedding-favours, and bouquets with streamers of white satin were on each box-ledge. The Royal box, as usual, occupied a considerable portion of the centre of

The Bride's Book

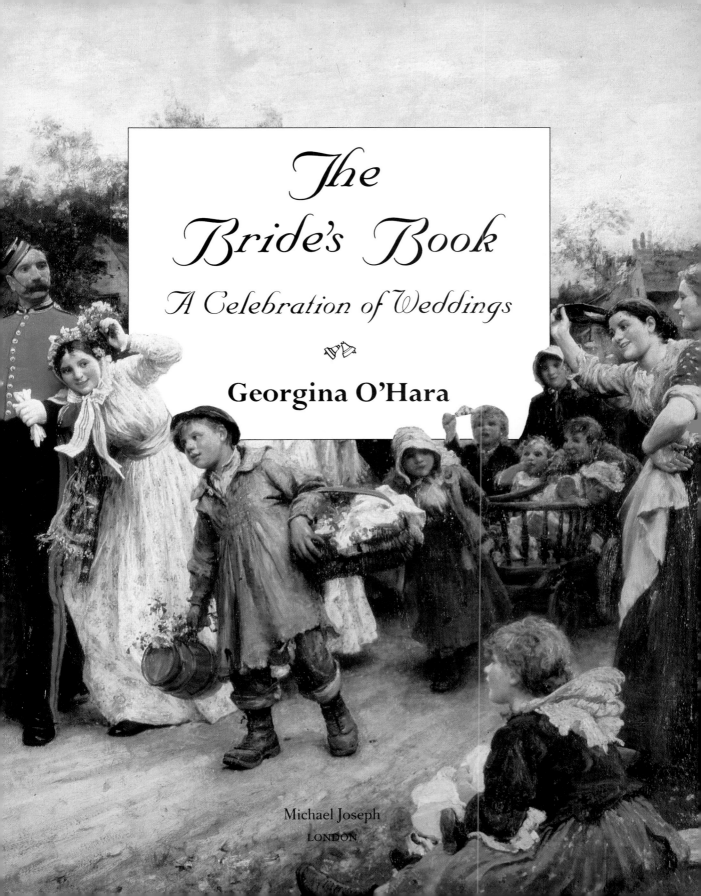

The Bride's Book

A Celebration of Weddings

Georgina O'Hara

Michael Joseph

LONDON

by the same author

MONEYWOMAN (Sphere)

ENCYCLOPAEDIA OF FASHION (Thames and Hudson)

THE WORLD OF THE BABY (Michael Joseph)

MICHAEL JOSEPH LTD

Published by the Penguin Group
27 Wrights Lane, London W8 5TZ, England
Viking Penguin Inc., 40 West 23rd Street, New York, New York 10010, USA
Penguin Books Australia Ltd, Ringwood, Victoria, Australia
Penguin Books Canada Ltd, 2801 John Street, Markham, Ontario, Canada L3R 1B4
Penguin Books (NZ) Ltd, 182-190 Wairau Road, Auckland 10, New Zealand

Penguin Books Ltd, Registered Offices: Harmondsworth, Middlesex, England

First published in Great Britain in 1991

Typeset in Linotron 11½ on 13pt Fournier
by Goodfellow & Egan Ltd, Cambridge
Printed and bound by Kyodo Printing, Singapore

ISBN 07181 3286 6

(*Endpapers*) Popular newspapers and periodicals of the nineteenth century gave extensive coverage to weddings of the British Royal Family. The Royal Wedding Number of *The Graphic* 10 July 1893, featured the marriage of the Duke of York and Princess Mary Victoria of Teck.

(*Title page*) In *The Village Wedding* nineteenth-century painter Sir Luke Fildes reflects on the joyous nature of a country wedding, an occasion which involved the entire community.

Contents

Introduction   7

The Ordination of Marriage   14

Consanguinity and Affinity   28

Putting Asunder   34

Sold for Sixpence   39

Dutiful Daughters   45

Merry Widows   72

A Bachelor's Life   78

The History of Courtship   86

Will You Marry Me?   96

Mergers and Acquisitions   114

Plans and Preparations   127

The Big Day   157

Wedding Anniversaries   187

Acknowledgements   189

Betrothed by W. Savage Cooper.

Introduction

YOU should never forget that marriage, which is a state that every young person ought to have in view, is a thing to last for life; and that, generally speaking, it is to make life happy or miserable; for, though a man may bring his mind to something nearly a state of indifference, even that is misery, except with those who can hardly be reckoned among sensitive beings.

William Cobbett, *Advice to a Lover*, 1840

Perhaps the easiest way to describe what this book is about is to state what it excludes. It is a book about brides and weddings, but it is not an etiquette book, nor does it suggest ways to go about setting up home. It is a book about marriage, but it is not a handbook or a social treatise on marital problems and their solutions. It offers no advice. To describe it as a social history would be misleading and a disservice to the excellent social historians working in the field of examining marital history. Yet it deals with English, and latterly American history, and it is also about an important aspect of our social lives, for it charts a course of proceedings that culminate in an event which is still, arguably, the most important day in the life of millions of women (and of course men), that day being their wedding day.

Today, we accept without question that we can marry whomsoever we choose – both parties being willing – because no woman alive can remember a time when things were any different. Certainly the marriages entered into by our great-great grandmothers would bear little resemblance to our own. I have questioned this acceptance and looked back through the ages to find out how, and why, we got to this point. Why did women marry? What was it like to be a bride in 1460, or 1620, or even 1850? Have brides always worn white wedding dresses? What is the symbolism of the wedding ring? Answering these and many other questions has resulted in a book which traces ancient traditions associated with the wedding ceremony and looks at the origin of the customs – many of which relate to pagan ritual – to which we still adhere today; and which examines how men and women and society in general viewed marriage.

From the Middle Ages the Church played a significant part in the wedding ceremony.

Due to the lack of material available prior to the Middle Ages, this period automatically lent itself as the background for the book, with the occasional nod further into the past to the Romans and early Germanic peoples when it was necessary to explain a precedent. And as I don't think it is possible to write a history book on contemporary matters, the book tails off in the early part of this century on which, from today's viewpoint at least, we have a perspective. It is my feeling that the sentiments of the people living at a certain time are best expressed by themselves: hence the inclusion of literature from various periods in history offering a broad selection of 'voices' – joyous, contemplative, resigned, rich or poor – which are used to illustrate marriage in all its guises through the ages.

It was necessary to explain at the beginning of the book the history of marriage: that is, the evolution of the custom and practice of marriage, the involvement of the Christian Church – which came to play a significant part in the wedding ceremony from the early Middle Ages – and the development of the legal aspects of marriage, and therefore divorce. Immediately it became obvious that some sort of parameters had to be set, as it would have been impossible to write about every kind of marriage in the world, and to include every religion. While I have settled broadly on the British Isles, there are many practices, peculiar to Scotland in particular, to include which would have narrowed the book to an examination of the differences between customs and laws in England and Scotland, which was not my intention.

In writing this book I had in mind someone, a woman – living in the British Isles or the United States of America, or other English-speaking countries where the laws have been adopted and adapted to suit local requirements – who is contemplating marriage. She may be about to be married. She might have been a bride already, and getting ready to embark on a second or third marriage. Or she may be someone who is very happily married, but who finds a strong fascination in the lives of women in former times – particularly aspects of their lives relating to weddings and marriages. And let's not forget the bride who on the eve of her wedding might be sufficiently curious to wonder how marriage was viewed – by men and women – in times past.

A wedding today may involve only two people, the bride and groom. If they are old enough they need not seek permission from their parents or guardians. Having a place to live or a job is not relevant to the marriage: all that's required is the money for a licence. The bride no longer requires a dowry: the couple will either bring their own household possessions to the marriage or rely on friends and relations to help them set up home with wedding gifts.

But this state of affairs would have been inconceivable less than two hundred years ago, when the bride and groom would have played the least significant parts in the marriage. Parents and relations would not only have instigated the negotiations for the marriage in the first place, but maintained control throughout the weeks or months of transactions – even to the extent of abandoning the match if the terms for the exchange of property and money could not be agreed upon. Relations and kinsmen were applied to for their approval of the match, presumably because the couple would require goodwill from them in the form of advice, connections and gifts.

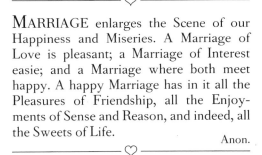

MARRIAGE enlarges the Scene of our Happiness and Miseries. A Marriage of Love is pleasant; a Marriage of Interest easie; and a Marriage where both meet happy. A happy Marriage has in it all the Pleasures of Friendship, all the Enjoyments of Sense and Reason, and indeed, all the Sweets of Life.

Anon.

For marriage, historically, was about the family. Since the word 'family' cannot be applied without evidence of children, marriage was also about having children (which it isn't necessarily today), about kinship, about heirs and about property. Medieval people viewed the family, rather than the individual, as the basic unit of economy: a view which continued to be held well into the seventeenth and even the eighteenth centuries. Two factors were essential to the longevity of the family; a large quantity of land and suitable marriages which provided heirs. In England, impartible inheritance in the Middle Ages not only undermined the value of women but also made male heirs essential, although if sons were not forthcoming, female children would suffice, for in the medieval peasant economy all children were valuable and by the age of seven they were part of the workforce. By custom even 'bride-children' – children who were born before the wedding – were legitimized on the wedding day.

Most European artists addressed the subject of marriage in their paintings. *Retrato de Una Joven Esposa* by Raimundo de Madrao y Garretta.

——— o ———

Marriage was also about power. Families, especially the land-owning aristocracy, have always depended upon marriage not only to provide necessary heirs but also for the support and protection that a network of alliances – aunts, uncles, cousins and the in-laws of the family into which one married – could all be relied upon to further mutual interests and defend the extended family against any common enemy in a manner which is quite unfamiliar to us today. Relatives could also act as lending agencies to each other, their loans secured by a complicated network of family connections. Marriage in former times was a far greater binding force than it is today, due largely to the efforts of the Church. Increasingly powerful from the early Middle Ages, the Church insisted on monagamous marriages and denied people the possibility of divorce. The Church decreed who could marry within closely related family units; and it forced weddings into the open, making the ceremony public and legitimizing heirs.

In order to understand anything at all about marriage in the past it is essential to have some sort of idea of the social conditions of the time under review. It is difficult to appreciate the motivations behind medieval marriage taken out of chronological context, for example, unless it is viewed against the backdrop of the feudal system.

——————— ᗢ ———————

THE Latinittes call it Coniugium, a toyning or yoking together, lyke as when two oxen are coupled under one yoke, they beare or draw together like burthen and weight.

Coverdale, *Christian State of Matrimony*, 1525

——————— ᗢ ———————

The imposition by the Normans of feudalism upon England had a significant effect on marriage in several ways, for the lord whose wife had to bear him a son to inherit his properties, and for the villein who was subject to the lord's jurisdiction, to whom he owed service and to whom he was required to pay fees or taxes when his daughter married. A free man could marry where and when he chose without regard to anyone else, but a man tied to a complex system of debt and payment had to take great care as to the choice of family with which he formed an alliance.

It is impossible to write about marriage and ignore the role of women and how much things have changed from the days of being married off to men with whom their fathers had struck a bargain, when they became the legal responsibility of their husbands with few rights of their own. Widowhood was often the first and only time women savoured any kind of freedom. In 1853, the state of women in marriage prompted the following view by Henry James, Horace Greely and Stephen Pearl Andrews in *Love, Marriage, and Divorce and the Sovereignty of the Individual:*

> The last thing that the husband is likely to know, in marriage that as it is, is the real state of the heart that throbs next him as he lays his head upon his own pillow. Woman, as well as the slave, must first be wholly free before she can afford to take the risk to speak freely. She dare not utter boldly her own complaint, and she will even denounce openly, while she prays fervently in secret, for the God-speed of the friend who does it for her.

Despite Church disapproval of a marriage taking place during Lent, the wedding of the Prince of Wales to Princess Alexandra took place in St George's Chapel in March 1863. *The Marriage of the Prince of Wales* by William Powell Frith.

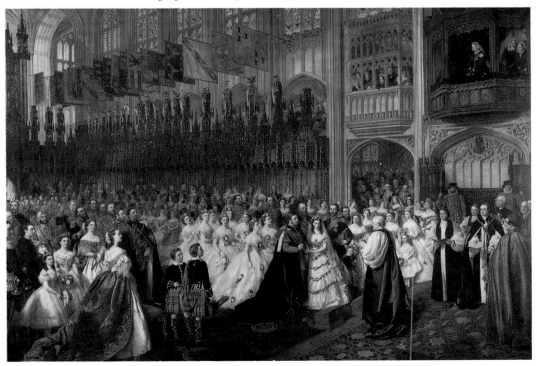

Nought beneath the sky
More sweet, more worthy is, than firm consent
Of man and wife in household government.
It joys their wishers-well, their enemies wounds
But to themselves the special good redounds.

George Chapman, *The Odyssey of Homer*

For whatever reasons people married (and many of their reasons are covered in this book), they were under no illusions about the nature of the arrangement. A good marriage comprised of three important parts: economic stability, political influence or the ability to tap into it in the terms of family alliances, and the birth of children. As long as husband and wife treated each other well, personal taste and happiness was not involved. However, even when marriage was contracted upon these terms, dissenting voices are sometimes heard, questioning the validity of a union that does not take into consideration the demands of human emotion and feeling, and marriages based on what seems to be a contemporary consideration – mutual love and affection – were unusual but by no means rare.

A great deal of the interest in a book like this lies in the comparison of the differences between the past and the present; and there is no doubt that marriage –

WITH the sound of King George's trumpets all the vain hopes of the weak and foolish young Pretender were blown away; and with that music, too, I may say, the drama of my own life was ended. That happiness, which hath subsequently crowned it, cannot be written in words; 'tis of its nature sacred and secret, and not to be spoken of, though the heart be ever so full of thankfulness, save the Heaven and the One Ear alone – to one fond being, the truest and tenderest and purest wife ever man was blessed with. As I think of the immense happiness which was in store for me, and of the depth and intensity of that love which, for so many years, hath blessed me, I own to a transport of wonder and gratitude for such a boon – nay, am thankful to have been endowed with a heart capable of feeling and knowing the immense beauty and value of the gift which God hath bestowed upon me. Sure, love *vincit omnia*; is immeasurably above all ambition, more precious than wealth, more noble than name. He knows not life who knows not that: he hath not felt the highest faculty of the soul who hath not enjoyed it. In the name of my wife I write the completion of hope, and the summit of happiness. To have such a love is the one blessing, in comparison of which all earthly joy is of no value; and to think of her, is to praise God.

W.M. Thackeray, *Henry Esmond*

both the motivation for and the business side of the arrangement – has changed enormously, with the greatest changes occurring during the last century. For many years, a verbal agreement was all that was required as a commitment to marry in the eyes of the Church, and medieval documents relate disputes between men and women over misunderstood intentions to marry. The modern version of this is the patrimony suit, when the woman testifies that the man said he loved her, wanted to marry her and have a child with her; only now the child is four years old, the couple never married and the woman is seeking financial support from the father of the child in recompense for breaking his word.

As the shape and form, and even the content, of marriage have changed, so has divorce. For as long as the concept of marriage for love has thrived in society, so have the demands for divorce increased. A divorce used to be almost impossible to obtain without involving the Church and the Crown at the highest levels. Between the 1600s and the 1830s – a time when calls were heard for love matches rather than arranged marriages – marriage in England was virtually indissoluble. Civil divorce was not possible until 1857, but it remained socially unacceptable for a long time after that with divorceés being refused permission to attend Court until the early part of this century. All that has changed: society has become more tolerant. Divorce rates in America approach half that of the number of marriages, with both young people and their parents seeking to dissolve their marriages. As people remarry families become extended with step-parents and step-children, half-brothers and sisters. Prenuptial contracts are featured increasingly in marriages today, in attempts to stamp out grounds for potential litigation between the parties.

AMERICANS, who make more of marrying for love than any people, also break up more of their marriages. This is not so much a failure of love as it is the determination of a people not to live without it.

Morton Hunt, *The Natural History of Love*

There is no doubt that marriage and divorce today are very different from marriage and divorce in the past. While people still marry for companionship, the framework of a marriage is not necessary if one wants to have children, nor is marriage regarded as just about the only career available to women for whom the alternative of spinsterhood – prior to this century – was viewed with a mixture of dread by those who approached it and pity by everyone else. But perhaps the most important change of all is that the majority of marriages today take place because the couple involved *love* each other.

The Ordination of Marriage

MARRIAGE according to the law of the
country is the union of one man with one
woman voluntarily entered into for life to
the exclusion of all others.

Notice in registry office

It is not only the motivations for marriage that were so different in the past but
the way in which people married. Marriage – in whatever form throughout the
world – was first intertribal and then exogamous, or outside the tribe, with the
earliest forms of exogamous marriage being marriage made by capture. The desire
and necessity for brides resulted in the abduction of women amongst early European
tribes for marriage purposes. Abduction lingered long in our history right through to
the Middle Ages when it was made illegal, but the pagan symbolism of abduction
remained embedded in wedding-day rituals, at least until the eighteenth century in the
rural parts of the British Isles when a bride was taken up on horseback by a close male
relative and chased by the groom and his men until she was 'caught'. The tradition of
the best man dates back to this early, probably tribal, ritual, suggesting that it was
with his help that the bridegroom captured his bride. It has been suggested also that
the old shoes, which it is the custom in some places to tie to the rear bumper of the car
in which the couple go away, were originally thrown after the abductor as he rode off
with his prize in a display of protest by the family of the bride. The honeymoon, it
was thought, was the time after the marriage when the husband negotiated a suitable
compensation with his wife's kinsmen in order to avoid a potential feud that could
result in acts of revenge and bloodshed.

Over the years the actual abduction was dispensed with and the next step in
marriage history which followed logically was marriage by purchase as the father of
the bride negotiated a substantial settlement for his daughter in advance, either in the
form of cash, property, cattle or a female relative of the groom for his own son.
Marriage by purchase was practised by the Barbarian tribes and the Anglo-Saxons.

Until the intervention of the Church in the early Middle Ages, marriages took place

Abducting the bride was a popular wedding custom in Wales even in the nineteenth century.

on the basis of verbal agreements, with or without a religious ceremony. 'Wedlock' is itself an Anglo-Saxon word, 'wed' meaning to assign property to the father of the bride in exchange for his daughter, while 'lock' means a pledge which was usually sealed by a ring. Very ancient betrothal ceremonies consisted of a verbal agreement on the terms of the marriage and the sealing of the bargain with a kiss and the placing of a ring on the woman's hand. The ring was seen as a sign that a bargain had been struck, and an indication not only that the woman was 'engaged' or otherwise unavailable for courtship, but also that the groom had demonstrated his intent to fulfil his promises. The betrothal ceremony, as it came to be known, was far more important than the actual wedding celebration itself, which was largely a matter of feasting and the conclusion of the deal with the bride returning to the groom's home. The betrothal ceremony took place in front of witnesses so that there was never any doubt in the future, in the absence of written records, that the event had actually taken place. The dowry of the bride was stated and the dower from the groom, if any, was also pronounced in front of witnesses. A practice called 'hand-fasting' or 'hand-fisting', a common-law ceremony, was also considered valid as a betrothal. In front of witnesses, the couple joined hands and pledged to marry each other. Troth-plight, as in the words of the marriage ceremony from the Church of England *Book of Common Prayer,* was another form of marriage which was considered valid. Troth-plighting was again verbal, with the couple speaking their vows to each other in the presence of witnesses. In many parts of Britain a child conceived between troth-plight – or the betrothal part of the marriage – and the actual wedding ceremony was considered to be legitimate.

A young couple exchange rings at their betrothal: an illumination from the
Très Riches Heures du Duc de Berry, 1413–16.

The betrothal was seen as the beginning of the marriage (not as today, when the wedding day itself is viewed as the start of the marriage), and it was therefore not unusual for the couple to begin sleeping together as man and wife before the actual nuptial ceremony. Indeed, in some societies, pre-marital sex, under the shield of the betrothal, was an essential part of the marriage ceremony. In time, as the betrothal ceased to be the most important aspect of the marriage, so it became appropriate for the couple to wait until the wedding before sharing a bed. In pre-medieval times, although in some parts of Europe the custom lingered until the sixteenth century, the bride was given a morning gift, or bridegift by the husband, usually in the form of jewellery, which served to confirm publicly her virginity and acknowledged the consummation of the marriage. The consummation of the marriage was an issue upon which Church leaders argued amongst themselves for years; they could not decide whether the betrothal was sufficient to validate the marriage or whether consummation was necessary.

———————— ◯ ————————

MARRIAGE customs have varied from age to age, from country to country, and from tribe to tribe; but each human unit, no matter how small, has had some definite plan for the orderly founding of a family and has frowned on all of its members who did not adhere to this plan.

Ira S. Wile, M.D. and Mary Day Winn,
Marriage in the Modern Manner, 1929

———————— ◯ ————————

Until fairly recently in our history the bride's consent to a marriage was not considered necessary. In Europe from early times to the Middle Ages the feelings of the bride in the matter of choosing a husband simply did not figure in the minds of her male or, for that matter, female relatives. As the property of her father or her closest male relative such as a brother or uncle, a girl was, by law, under his jurisdiction. Under Roman law, however, the consent of both parties – which today we take for granted – was specifically required (and, as such, was a practice ahead of its time; in many respects Roman women were treated better than women of the Barbarian tribes). The practice of consent came about under the influence of Christianity, which had adopted it from Roman Law. Initially the consent aspect was parental consent required from the parents for the marriages of their daughters and sons: this was designed to prevent an heir or heiress contracting what was seen by the parents to be a bad marriage. In time, in all societies, consent came to mean the consent of the bride herself. Many brides were forced into marriages against their wills, and the Church took a stand against this practice by demanding at the beginning of the wedding ceremony if the parties consented to the marriage. This part of the service is retained today.

By the eleventh century both ecclesiastical and civil authorities recognized a marriage as valid only if both parties had consented freely to it. By asking the consent of the couple the authorities intended to avoid marriages forced upon young people by ambitious parents or, in the case of vassals, by their lords. In time, the Church arranged for the annulment of a marriage to which a girl, if she was at least fifteen, had not given her consent.

Marriage as we think of it today dates back only as far as the early Middle Ages. For although the Christian church had been in existence for much longer and had been able to exert influence over marriage – for instance, the presence of a priest at a wedding ceremony was encouraged but by no means accepted – it had not been able to use its powers to gain control. Under the Romans the civil authorities exercised jurisdiction over marriage but as Christianity spread through the Empire the Church was granted some judicial power which it was permitted to use in a disciplinary sense rather than in legislative control. Christian principles were slowly absorbed by Roman Law and during the reign of the Frankish kings the Church gained increasing authority over marriage by arguing that as it was a religious ceremony marriage should be under the jurisdiction of the church rather than the state.

By degrees the Church addressed itself to every part of marriage from stressing the importance of consent to taking a stance on the level of degrees of consanguinity. The Church was impeded in its authority over marriage not only in the slow acceptance by people of the religious nature of marriage and of church doctrine, but also by the conflicts found within the Old and New Testaments, which were the basis of much argument for centuries. The Old Testament stressed fecundity and forbade adultery and incest, yet some Old Testament figures practised polygamy and had concubines; divorce was available to men only. The New Testament, on the other hand, found marriage to be indissoluble except as found in Matthew 19:9: 'Whosoever shall put away his wife except for fornication, and shall marry another, committeth adultery', and encouraged both virginity and monogamy. Regardless of all the arguing by Church leaders over the exact details, the Church's stance on marriage was clear from the beginning in that it restricted sexual licence and encouraged marriage, seeing it as the only condition under which sexual activity could occur.

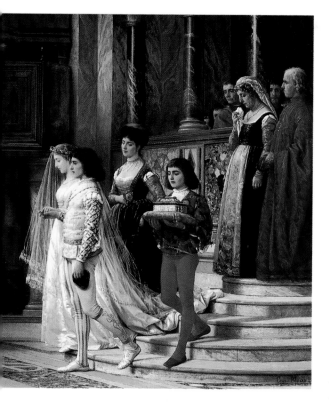

The Marriage by Eugene von de Blaas.

Although the Romans, Barbarians and the Christians disagreed on various aspects of marriage there was mutual agreement on the importance of the incest taboo and the value of the family unit. However, Romans and Barbarians permitted that unit to be broken by allowing men to divorce their wives; and the ability to instigate divorce was available later to Roman women too, especially wealthy women. Roman men were also allowed sexual freedom of maintaining concubines, and remarrying after divorce which the Church firmly denied both sexes. According to the Church, marriage was for the duration of the joint lives of the husband and wife, but in times of high mortality and in the face of the people's desires the Church reluctantly admitted the remarriage of a widow or widower, although it stood firm against the idea of the dissolution of the marriage.

This principle was challenged by the problems encountered by the partners of those who committed adultery, those who were found to be heretics, and by those who suffered great cruelty at the hands of their spouse, not to mention the desires of royalty who often wished to trade one wife for another in the search for an heir. As a result the Church, acting more like a marriage counsellor than a judge, arranged separations between couples, or, in the case of royalty and nobility, allowed annulments to be purchased, a practice that in later years brought heavy criticism on Church leaders by religious reformers.

It was not unknown for the Church's attempts to regulate marriage to be carried to an extreme. In the seventh and eighth centuries it ruled that couples were to abstain from sex or 'meeting' with their wives forty days before Christmas, forty days before Easter, eight days after Pentecost, on the eve of great feasts, on Sundays, Wednesdays and Fridays, during the wife's menstruation and pregnancy, thirty days after the birth of a boy, forty days after the birth of a girl and five days before taking communion. A man who 'met' his wife on any of the above occasions was fined but if he was drunk at the time his fine was reduced. The Church relied on guilty feelings and the fear of divine retribution for the men to confess their sins.

One of the most important issues to the Church was the publication of the marriage. In this way it sought not only to inhibit abductions, but to prevent marriage within the forbidden degrees of consanguinity and to ensure the endowment of the bride in front of witnesses. But the Church had to wait several centuries before it was able to prohibit clandestine marriages and insist on the publication of the marriage ceremony. The Church put the priest forward, giving to him the task of not only reading the banns but directing that he was to be included in all aspects of the wedding ceremony. This helped to shift the emphasis away from the betrothal to the wedding ceremony itself. The priest was also called upon to arbitrate in any subsequent problems arising over the validity of the betrothal and the rights of the couple to marry. Once the couple were present at church the ceremony took place in the porch doorway so that as many people as possible would hear the financial details of the marriage and witness the couple speaking their vows.

The church porch or doorway played a far more important role in history than it does today, when the significance is all but forgotten. It may be strange for us to realize now, but most wedding ceremonies took place *outside* the church and the parties did not enter the church until they were married. When Edward I married Marguerite of France in 1299 she was endowed at the door of Canterbury Cathedral. In 1554 the Bishop of Paris performed the wedding ceremony of Mary, daughter of Henry VIII, to Philip II of Spain at the doorway of the cathedral of Notre Dame, which was also the site, some forty or so years later, for the marriage by proxy of Charles I to Henrietta Maria of France.

In 1215 the Magna Carta upheld the powers of the Church of England over marriage related subjects such as dowries, heirships and annulments. The Church called for the reading of the banns, consent of both parties and public weddings with the endowment of the bride at the church door. As Frances and Joseph Gies summed up in *Marriage and the Family in the Middle Ages,* 'In the year 500 the Church could only protest and admonish; in the year 1000 it could threaten and command.' Although it took almost one thousand years to establish, the power held by the Church in the thirteenth century would have been unrecognizable to the Romans and Barbarians. Ecclesiastical courts held rights and privileges denied to them in earlier centuries and there was no doubt that the courts were busy. While church marriage was recognized as licit, the Church had to accept that other types of marriage were also valid or be faced with invalidating a great number of marriages of the population whose marriages, and those of the generations before them, had been carried out without the benefit of the Christian marriage ceremony. In addition, the Church had to accept that private clandestine marriages might also be valid if the couple had spoken their vows even without the presence of witnesses for, in its own words, in order for a marriage to be valid it required the consent of both parties. But problems lay in the denial by one party or the other that the actual vows had been spoken, or that they had agreed to the marriage in the first place, or with parents who desired to see their children's marriages annulled on the basis that the partner was considered unsuitable or that the child was too young.

The age at marriage was of considerable importance, people marrying at a younger age than they do today. Under the Romans the age of consent to marriage was twelve

A young couple apply to the priest to marry them. *Coming to Get Married,* An 1843
engraving after the painting by Geirnaert.

years for girls and fourteen years for boys. In the years following the Roman Empire
the age dropped so that no marriage could be contracted for children under seven
years of age, and those marriages could be repudiated by children once they reached
the ages of twelve for girls and fourteen for boys. Royal marriages and those between
powerful ruling families took place at extraordinary early ages for political reasons to
secure territories. In November, 1160, Henry, son of Henry II of England and Eleanor
of Aquitaine, married Margaret, daughter of Eleanor's ex-husband Louis VII of
France and his new wife, Constance of Castile. Both were aged five. Isabella,
daughter of the Duke of Ferrara and Modena, was betrothed in 1480 at the age of six
to Gianfrancesco Gonzaga of Mantua, who was eight years older, although they were
not married for ten years.

However, it was felt by some Church authorities, presumably those whose
loyalties lay with certain noble families, in an attempt at compromise, that a child of
nine and a half years was capable of giving consent to a marriage.

The age of consent for girls being at twelve years and for boys being at fourteen
years continued throughout the Middle Ages until 1753 when the passing of
Hardwicke's Marriage Act set the age of consent at twenty-one. This was an attempt
to stamp out clandestine marriages between people younger than twenty-one years
who were now required to seek the consent of their parents to the marriage unless
they were already a widow or widower. This Act was repealed in 1823. In 1929 the
Age of Marriage Act made marriages under sixteen invalid and required parents to
give their consent.

In the USA some states retained until the twentieth century the laws that gave girls
at the age of twelve and boys at the age of fourteen the ability to consent to marriage,

Victorian painter William Powell Frith captures family life in his *For Better, For Worse*.

although the majority of states had, by the mid-nineteenth century, adopted a law which stated that children could marry at the age of sixteen with the consent of their parents or eighteen without the consent of their parents.

Although Roman girls and boys were technically able to marry at the ages of twelve and thirteen scholars believe that most boys married much later while girls married somewhere in their teens with nineteen being considered late. The idea that nineteen years of age was late for a girl fluctuated over the centuries. It is impossible to say with any kind of accuracy exactly at what age people did marry, for records for this sort of information were not kept, but historians who have addressed this subject have drawn certain conclusions. Given the relatively short life expectancy of people in the past it should not be surprising if they married early. However, it seems that the marriage age rose in times of prosperity and dropped dramatically after such devastating calamities as the Black Death in 1349. Once the population had reproduced itself, marriage age levels rose again, as they did in the fifteenth century.

Following the Middle Ages people began to marry later, and by Victorian times many girls were well into the twenties before marrying. The age at marriage has also been linked to the economic situations of the parties concerned. For example, working class people were thought to delay marriage until they could afford homes of their own. Without contraception early marriage would bring many children, thus diminishing the chances of affording a home or improving one's situation in life. The middle classes and tradesmen, who needed to establish themselves before they could find the resources for the expense of the kind of marriage that would be expected of them, also delayed marriage. In addition, women from the middle and upper classes expected to be maintained in the same fashion as they had been used to in the household of their parents, and it would take a man a good number of years to reach that level should he require a wife from a similar class or station in life to his own.

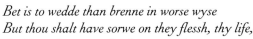

Bet is to wedde than brenne in worse wyse
But thou shalt have sorwe on they flessh, thy life,
And bers thy wyves thral, as seyn these wyse.

Geoffrey Chaucer

By the fifteenth century the Church in England had reached the zenith of its powers before the Protestant Reformers implemented changes in both attitudes to marriage and actual marriage laws. The Reformers promoted the idea that marriage was a secular contract and that it should not be considered the sacrament proposed by the Church; if marriage was a contract, they said, then it should be dissoluble. The Protestant doctrines were formed in a report submitted to Edward VI and although no changes were made to canon law it seems that between 1552 and 1602 the Church courts adopted the principles of the Reformation and permitted divorces and new marriages. In 1603, in the reign of Elizabeth I, the situation was regulated under a

The marriage certificate of Princess Victoria Patricia Helen Elizabeth of Connaught to Alexander Maule Robert Ramsey on 17 February 1919, witnessed by the King and Queen.

Statute and marriage once more became indissoluble until 1857 when marriage and divorce became a civil matter.

Following the Reformation Puritans too regarded marriage as secular and that therefore problems arising from marriage should be dealt with by civil courts. During the Commonwealth (1649–58) marriage was declared a civil ceremony and the use of the Book of Common Prayer was forbidden, until after the Restoration when people were once more able to choose a religious ceremony.

It would be several centuries before the Reformers' ideas were implemented. In American states marriage was viewed as a civil contract, not a sacrament as in the 'old country'. The ceremony could be performed by a magistrate – as it is still possible today – and the marriage was subject to civil laws but churches nonetheless became involved in family matters.

During the seventeenth century incidences of clandestine marriages rose dramatically in England. Although marriages in such places in London as the Fleet, May Fair, the Savoy and in Edinburgh at Canongate, had thrived since the early 1600s they increased in number throughout the century. These clandestine marriages were carried out by priests who provided a licence and certificate, and often the loan of a ring, for a guinea or so. Clandestine weddings were sought by those who wished to avoid the publicity of a church wedding and the reading of the banns, people who had encountered parental opposition to their marriages, runaway heiresses, fortune hunters, those marrying without parental consent, bigamists, or those who could not afford a church wedding. To the participants the appeal of marriages at the Fleet and other places was the instant availability, the low cost and the relative anonymity. Of course, an unwilling heiress could be forced into a Fleet marriage without the presiding priest asking too many questions such as whether she consented to the match. Although technically the marriage was invalid the shame of the heiress and her family – especially if the marriage had been consummated – sometimes meant that the offending husband was not punished. It was during this time that many of the famous Gretna Green marriages took place. As Scottish law only required a witnessed declaration of marriage many couples, who had encountered parental opposition, took off for the Scottish border town, often with their family in hot pursuit. In 1753 Lord Hardwicke's Marriage Act made clandestine marriages illegal, giving the church wedding legal precedence over the spoken unwitnessed vows or espousals.

KINGDOM OF SCOTLAND,

COUNTY OF DUMFRIES,

PARISH OF GRETNA.

These are to Certify, to all whom they may concern: That _Thomas Jones_ from the Parish of _Wylam_ in the County of _Durham_ and _Sarah Watkins_ from the Parish of _Burslem-on-Stoke_ in the County of _Durham_ being now both here present, and having declared to me that they are Single Persons, have now been Married after the manner of the Laws of Scotland: As witness our hands at Gretna, this _Twenty fifth_ Day of _December 1819_

signed _Andrew Elliot Gretna_

Witnesses, { × _Stephen Slough, Postboy._
× _Walter Parlane, Stableman_

Thomas Jones and Sarah Watkins, both from Durham, crossed the border to Scotland to be married at Gretna Green in December of 1819.

——— o ———

The Act also made it unlawful for people under twenty-one years to marry without their parents' consent. By the nineteenth century it was no longer necessary for people who had met with opposition to their marriage to travel as far as Scotland because after 1837 the couple could stand before the civil registrar and legally be married.

It is interesting to note, however, that marriage was not considered essential by everyone. The increasingly industrialized society of the nineteenth century threw young men and women together in a way which inevitably produced a relaxation in the modes of courtship. In poor areas common-law husbands and wives were an accepted aspect of daily life. For a woman in particular there was a certain appeal to being a common-law wife. She could continue to work without being legally obliged to hand over her earnings to her husband, living together avoided the expense of a wedding and both parties were free to leave should major disagreements arise. Many parties to common law marriages had been previously married and could not divorce, but chose to live with someone rather than being convicted of bigamy.

THE WIFE OF BATH'S PROLOGUE

'If there were no authority on earth
Except experience, mine, for what it's worth,
And that's enough for me, all goes to show
That marriage is a misery and a woe;
For let me say, if I may make so bold,
My lords, since when I was but twelve years old,
Thanks be to God Eternal evermore,
Five husbands have I had at the church door;
Yes, it's a fact that I have had so many,
All worthy in their way, as good as any.

*   'Someone said recently for my persuasion*
That as Christ only went on one occasion
To grace a wedding – in Cana of Galilee –
He taught me by example there to see
That it is wrong to marry more than once.
Consider, too, how sharply, for the nonce,
He spoke, rebuking the Samaritan
Beside the well, Christ Jesus, God and man.

"Thou has had five men husband unto thee
And he that even now thou hast," said He,
"Is not thy husband." Such the words that fell;
But what He meant thereby I cannot tell,
Why was her fifth – explain it if you can –
No lawful spouse to the Samaritan?
How many might have had her, then, to wife?
I've never heard an answer all my life
To give the number final definition.
People may guess or frame a supposition,
But I can say for certain, it's no lie,
God bade us all to wax and multiply.
That kindly text I well can understand.
Is not my husband under God's command
To leave his father and mother and take me?
No word of what the number was to be,
Then why not marry two or even eight?
And why speak evil of the married state?

The wedding of Boccaccio Adimani to Lisa Ricasoli was an occasion for a great display of wealth and extravagance during the fourteenth century.

'Take wise King Solomon of long ago;
We hear he had a thousand wives or so.
And would to God it were allowed to me
To be refreshed, aye, half so much as he!
He must have had a gift of God for wives,
No one to match him in a world of lives!
This noble king, one may as well admit,
On the first night threw many a merry fit
With each of them, he was so much alive.
Blessed be God that I have wedded five!
Welcome the sixth, whenever he appears.
I can't keep continent for years and years.
No sooner than one husband's dead and gone
Some other Christian man shall take me on,
For them, so says the Apostle, I am free
To wed, o'God's name, where it pleases me.
Wedding's no sin, so far as I can learn.
Better it is to marry than to burn,

'What do I care if people choose to see
Scandal in Lamech for his bigamy?
I know that Abraham was a holy man
And Jacob too – I speak as best I can –
Yet each of them, we know, had several brides,
Like many another holy man besides.
Show me a time or text where God disparages
Or sets a prohibition upon marriages
Expressly, let me have it! Show it me!
And where did He command virginity?
I know as well as you do, never doubt it,
All the Apostle Paul has said about it;
He said that as for precepts he had none.
One may advise a woman to be one;
Advice is no commandment in my view.
He left it in our judgement what to do.'

Geoffrey Chaucer, *The Canterbury Tales*

CONSANGUINITY AND AFFINITY

One of the reasons why banns are read today, and the priest asks in the wedding service if anyone knows of an impediment as to why the couple cannot be married, is that in the past there were many more restrictions about whom one might marry than there are today. Some of these restrictions, established first by custom then taken up by the Church and the state, resulted from human preoccupation with the incest taboo, the question of who could marry within the familial structure. Customary laws were the cumulative result of the laws of the Romans, the Germanic peoples, the Visigoths, the Franks and the Saxons, adapted and altered in different geographical areas not only in England but throughout Europe. The prohibition rules against marriage, which varied under successive invaders, were due either to consanguinity (blood) or affinity (marriage). There were also civil prohibitions due to insanity of one party or the existence of a previous marriage, premarital impotence, or one party having taken vows of chastity or holy orders. A person who had plotted to murder a married person in order to marry the spouse was also forbidden to marry, as was the collaborator. A dispensation from the Church was required for people of different religions who wished to marry.

The Egyptians, we know, allowed brother and sister to be married to each other. By Roman times marriages between people related to the fourth degree (that is oneself, father/mother, grandfather/grandmother, uncle/aunt, nephew/niece) were forbidden. Emperor Claudius found this law inconvenient in AD 41 when he wanted to marry his niece Agrippina, so he had the Senate redefine the rules of consanguinity. But in general, the laws of the Romans, Barbarians and Christians agreed with the definition of incest and the consanguinity tables which extended to the fourth degree.

By the sixth century, wherever Christianity was practised, the Church had stepped in to declare that first cousins were unable to marry; this appeared to have been a flexible point until this time, with the Church providing dispensations for those wealthy and powerful enough to seek them. In the following century, after a council ruling, the Church – playing an increasingly prominent role in marriage law – included spiritual kin, godparents and godchildren as being forbidden marriage partners.

It is important to note here the concept of kinship that existed in the early medieval years. Today we think of our kin as being those related to us by blood or marriage, tracing the relationships bilaterally from both father and mother. But then the Church held that husband and wife became One upon marriage, thus all one's husband's relatives became one's own, as did all the relatives of a

Consanguinity tables from the Middle Ages, dated 1012.

wife for the husband. The separateness of husband and wife is a twentieth-century concept. Some societies excluded illegitimate children from family kin; others maintained that children were legitimate even if their parents' marriages ended on the grounds of affinity or consanguinity. In the Middle Ages, as Barbara Hanawalt records in *The Ties That Bound,*

> Common law and church law differed from customary law but were also generous in recognizing the legitimacy of children. If a marriage ended on the grounds of affinity or consanguinity, the children were considered legitimate. Even a child produced from an adulterous union in the fifteenth century was deemed legitimate. Although customs varied from manor to manor, the strong sentiment that property should descend to the person with the closest blood tie remained firm.

Yet other societies considered as kin those with whom they had spiritual relationships, such as godparents and godchildren. In the eighth century the English missionary St Boniface recommended that consanguinity be redefined as extending to the seventh degree. The Frankish King Pepin supported St Boniface, who was the papal legate to the Frankish church, seeing a way to prevent his nobles forming strong dynastic alliances and then rising up against him, and the recommendation became law. Boniface also decreed that a man who had sexual relations with a woman could not subsequently marry any of her kinsfolk. Curiously enough, people adhered to this rule for a number of centuries, although it appears, by the sixteenth century, not to have been enforced. Like many laws during the Middle Ages, this one was open to local interpretation. The Church was unable to impose its laws concerning marriage on small rural communities where custom tended to take precedence.

By the early Middle Ages throughout Europe marriage within the seventh degree of kinship was forbidden. This meant that finding someone to marry in a small village must have been a problem since in outlying agricultural areas most people were related to each other in some way. However, even though the priest might ask at the church door if anyone knew of an impediment to the marriage, in the absence of written records most people would not know, or could not remember to whom they were related.

As the Church began to play an increasingly powerful role, reaching its zenith in the twelfth and thirteenth centuries, both in marriage litigation and the wedding ceremony itself, throughout Europe Church leaders found themselves in direct conflict with kings and the nobility who, if they wanted to rid themselves of a spouse and finding divorce impossible to achieve, sought annulment on the grounds of consanguinity or affinity.

A number of religious leaders spoke out about consanguinity, each one assuming a different interpretation of the Bible. The major problem involved resolving the conflicting information contained within the Bible itself, and the lack of clarity as to whether the prohibitions referred to marriage, intercourse or widows, who were treated as a separate case. In 1215 the Fourth Lutheran Council, convened by Innocent III, put back the forbidden degrees to the fourth degree so that people who descended from the same great-great-grandfather could not marry; or, to put it another way, a person could not marry his own or his wife's third cousin, or any nearer relative. The fourth degree still included godparents and godchildren, but dispensations were available to those who had the wherewithal to acquire them from the Church.

In the twelfth century when King Louis VII and his queen, Eleanor of Aquitaine, planned to separate, they persuaded the Archbishop of Sens to sanction an annulment – despite the birth of two daughters – on the grounds that Louis and Eleanor were third cousins and had therefore married within the forbidden degrees of kinship. Eleanor then turned round and married Henry of England in 1152 to whom she was no less related than Louis.

Henry VIII's struggles with the Church ultimately affected the history of

Eighteenth-century illustration to *Grandison,* by Richardson, showing a couple kneeling before the minister (Anon.).

England. In order to marry his first wife, Catherine of Aragon, the former wife of his brother, Arthur, Henry managed to get special dispensation from the Pope. The king confronted the Church once again with his attempts to dispose of Catherine, who had been unable to provide him with an heir, so that he could marry Anne Boleyn. He claimed that Catherine had lied and that she had in fact been married to Arthur, but Pope Clement VII, who was being held captive by Catherine's nephew, the Emperor Charles V, would not submit to Henry's demands. Determined to marry Anne Boleyn, Henry denied papal authority in England and made himself Governor of the Church of England. The Archbishop of Canterbury, Thomas Cranmer, and the Lord Privy Seal, Thomas Cromwell, were called upon to announce Henry's divorce, and shortly afterwards Henry married Anne Boleyn.

The monarch whose quest for a male heir took him through six marriages effected another change when he wanted to divorce his fourth wife, Anne of Cleves, on the grounds of non-consummation. He wished at the time to marry Catherine Howard, who was his second wife's cousin and therefore forbidden to him in marriage under the rules of affinity. As a result Henry legalized marriage to all first cousins in 1540.

During the Reformation that followed Henry VIII's actions the rules of consanguinity and affinity were changed once more. The great religious movement was aimed at reforming the practices of the Church of Rome and establishing reformed or Protestant churches in central and north-west Europe. When in the 1520s Luther condemned the Catholic Church, he denounced the practice of upholding rigid consanguinity and affinity laws on the one hand and the lucrative business of selling dispensations on the other. According to Luther, the recommended laws were based on Leviticus 18 where twelve people one might not marry are listed. Other reformers disagreed. The ultimate result was that in various parts of Europe the laws were changed, dropping many of the impediments, so that the marriage laws became clearer and less subject to the vagaries of local interpretation. In essence the Reformation put back the laws to the way they were prior to the sixth century. In his book *Marriage and Love in England 1300–1840,* Alan Macfarlane summarizes the laws concerning marriage impediments:

> Basically, with one small exception, the rules concerning which kin one may or may not marry are the same in England today as they were in 1540. The exception is that in 1907 it became legal to marry a deceased wife's sister. Otherwise there have been no changes from a situation which allows marriage of all but very close relatives. Essentially one may marry all except members of the nuclear family and all those, including uncles and aunts, nephews and nieces, in the ascending and descending generations. First cousin marriage is now, as it was from 1540, legal, if often disapproved of. At marriage the couple became 'one blood'. Thus a man was forbidden from marrying the same range of wife's kin as of his own blood relatives. For instance, he could not marry his wife's aunt even though she was not a blood relative. The prohibitions continued after the spouse's death. Hence marriage with a deceased wife's sister was forbidden.

In 1865 the Pre-Raphaelite painter William Holman Hunt was obliged to marry Edith, sister of his deceased first wife, Fanny, in Switzerland as under the laws of England the marriage would have been illegal.

In America the rules prohibiting marriage are based on those of the Church of England – with the exception of those laws relating to Jews. Although a number of states still prohibit first-cousin marriages, the courts have stated that such marriages will be recognized if performed in a state where it is legal because such a union does not cause 'much social alarm'. In 1974 the Uniform Marriage and Divorce Act prohibited marriage between an ancestor and a descendant, or between a brother and sister, whether the relationship is by the half or the whole blood, or by adoption; and a marriage between an uncle and a niece or between an aunt and a nephew, whether the relationship is by the half or the whole blood, except as to marriages permitted by the established customs of aboriginal cultures (i.e. earliest known inhabitants). The Act eliminated most of the traditional marriage prohibitions and all affinity prohibitions. It permitted first-cousin marriage, but uncle/niece and aunt/nephew were prohibited except in circumstances relating to the customs of early cultures. Marriage of brothers and sisters by adoption are prohibited because of social interest in discouraging romantic attachments between such persons even if there is no genetic risk involved. The Act does not prohibit uncle/niece and aunt/nephew marriages where an adoption has created the relationship.

Medieval weddings were often very lavish and formal affairs. Here Philip 'The Good' of Burgundy marries Isabel of Portugal in 1430 seen through the eyes of an anonymous seventeenth-century painter.

PUTTING ASUNDER

Whilst this is not the place for a discussion of the reasons and causes of divorce, it is appropriate to look at the history of divorce in a book about marriage for just as marriage has changed enormously over the centuries so has divorce and the ability to remarry. Many people reading this book will be marrying for the second or third time, which would have been unthinkable one hundred and fifty years ago unless one had been widowed. American divorce law based on the desires of the people has contributed a great deal to the attitudes towards divorce throughout the Western world, for in America there is no social stigma attached to divorce; if one marriage doesn't work out it is acceptable practice to end it and try one's luck with someone else.

> *Eaper, Weaper, chimbley-sweeper,*
> *Had a wife but couldn't keep her,*
> *Had annover, didn't love her,*
> *Up the chimbley he did shove her.*
>
> Old English rhyme

Divorce laws in America vary a great deal in any case and this has much to do with the fact that divorce is regulated by the state and not by federal courts, and the difference in religions of the settlers of the original thirteen colonies. During the 1600s the North Eastern colonies were settled primarily by followers of the Protestant Reformation and they permitted divorce under the following circumstances: fraudulent marriage contract, consanguinity, bigamy, impotence, desertion and adultery. The mid-Atlantic states did permit divorce but it was less common, while the southern states did not permit divorce but allowed a separation of bed and board along European lines. After the Revolution the States became more liberal in their attitudes to divorce permitting a time span of separation and mutual agreement as reasons for divorce.

But it took Europe centuries to accept divorce as being a facet of marriage because the Church viewed marriage as basically indissoluble. From medieval times to the nineteenth century one third of the people marrying were doing so for the second or third time, not because they had divorced, but because of the death of a spouse. The view that marriage was indissoluble and that it should last for the duration of the joint lives of the partners had to be modified so that the Church allowed remarriage after the death of one partner, echoed in the words of the marriage service 'until death us do part'.

The Tiff (Anon.): marriage plans did not always go smoothly.

Even so, divorce, of one form or another, has always been available, but under various conditions. At different times over the centuries divorce could have been instigated by the husband (rarely by the wife), by the couple jointly (mutual consent), or by the Church or state. Some of the reasons for divorce that we take for granted today, such as desertion or cruelty, were not incorporated into law until the fifteenth and sixteenth centuries.

The history of divorce is really the story of the Church's long struggle to deny divorce to people who wished to be able to divorce their spouses. Under Roman law termination of a marriage was possible and usually easier for the husband than the wife. Men were required to seek approval from their families but towards the end of Roman rule husbands were able to divorce their wives at will, without having to cite adultery or the common pretext of attempted poisoning. Divorce by mutual consent was also possible, especially for the wealthy. Wealthy wives found that they could dispose of their husbands more easily than poorer wives. The general status of women after the Roman period disintegrated throughout Europe. Men could divorce their wives, but women could not divorce their husbands. Under Germanic law codes men were able to divorce their wives not only for adultery but also for barrenness, or any illness which prevented a wife from fulfilling her conjugal duty.

The Church coming to power in the early Middle Ages reinforced the status of men over women, yet, as with the issue of consanguinity the Biblical sources concerning divorce, to which Church leaders referred, were confusing. Divorce was available to men but not to women according to interpreters of the Old Testament. Adultery was forbidden despite the fact that the Old Testament contained evidence of concubinage and polygamy. Marriage law according to the New Testament, on the other hand, was formulated from 'Whosoever shall put away his wife, except it be for fornication, and shall marry another, committeth adultery' (Matthew 19:9), which left marriage otherwise indissoluble.

Church doctrine was directly opposed by kings and nobles of the early Middle Ages who wished to retain the right to divorce at will, and to dispose of their wives on any grounds they found appropriate. The wishes of the kings to arrange marriages to suit their own desires – whether the need was sexual, for heirs, or to marry to bring about changes in political alliances – were not condemned by the general populace, many of whom wished to divorce themselves. It wasn't until the last half of the eighth century that the Church was forced to acknowledge certain grounds for divorce and eventual remarriage. While it did not consider mutual consent to be a valid reason for divorce, the Church did agree that lack of consent to the marriage, adultery, impotence, leprosy or one party becoming a nun or monk, could be considered reasonable grounds for divorce. (The Church was concerned about remarriage and the protection of the rights of inheritance of the children of the first marriage.) As we have seen, kings and nobles, who could not justify divorce on any of the above grounds, turned to the Church's rules of consanguinity and affinity which they found useful tools for the manipulation of their divorces, or annulments as they were called, although the couples had been married for years and produced children together. The medieval church permitted divorce *a vinculo*, which was an annulment, a statement which declared that the marriage had never existed.

By the end of the Middle Ages, as the Church sought to control all aspects of marriage the task of mediating in relationships fell to the priest, who was not only involved in the publication of the marriage and was therefore the arbiter in the case of possible impediments, and in the content and form of the wedding service, but also intervened in marital disputes.

As the Church regulated marriage it attempted, too, to regulate divorce – or at least separation. Ecclesiastical courts were established which, working alone or with lay authorities, orchestrated many separations between unhappy couples. Divorce *a mensa et thoro* was a separation from 'bed and board' and permitted the couple to live apart but not to remarry. Formal separation of this kind was not uncommon and separations on the grounds of cruelty, adultery or impotence were arranged by the Church courts. Informal separation often took place amongst the peasantry but not amongst anyone wealthier, whose property considerations would have required recourse to a formal written separation.

Due to their geographical and social isolation parts of Britain were untouched by the Church courts, and here local custom ruled dictating that husbands and wives were free to marry again if the spouse had deserted them for seven years, if the spouse was reputed to be dead, or if one spouse was consistently unfaithful. These divorces were arranged between the husband and wife concerned and witnessed by friends and relatives, many of whom had witnessed the marriage. The people involved in these self-styled divorces believed them to be valid. Local customs, many dating back to pre-Roman times, provided a headache for the Church for centuries. Whole clans of families had married and

During the nineteenth century arranged marriages fell out of favour. *Mariage de Convenance I* (above) and *Mariage de Convenance – After* by Sir William Quiller Orchardson.

divorced or separated according to their own beliefs and customs and to invalidate these unions would have been impossible.

One custom found in rural parts of England until the mid-nineteenth century, and amongst the slaves of the southern United States, was the 'besom wedding' or 'jumping the broom'. A birch branch or broom handle was set up across the doorway to a house. The groom first jumped over the branch, followed by the bride. If either bride or groom touched the branch when jumping over it the marriage was not considered valid. By jumping backwards over the branch the couple could break the marriage, but this irrevocable step had to be taken within the first year and was usually done so if the couple found themselves unable to have children or incompatible in other ways. On both occasions the procedure was watched by witnesses who could later testify should arguments follow.

In England, from the tenth century until 1857 when civil divorce became possible, the Church controlled marriage and divorce forbidding divorce with a right to remarry. In spite of the efforts of the Reformers who declared marriage to be a civil contract which, they argued, could thus be broken, divorce was only obtainable as an annulment, at a price, or the couple could be separated, but nothing approximated contemporary divorce. From the late seventeenth century it became possible to divorce by an Act of Parliament but the cost of such a venture resulted in few divorces and then only the very wealthy and very powerful were able to avail themselves of this facility.

Marriage the happiest State of Life would be
If Hands were only join'd where Hearts agree.

Anon.

Increasingly the Church had to accept the impossibility of two unhappy people living together in harmony for years, and it was the Church in the twentieth century that ultimately suggested that marital breakdown be a valid reason for the dissolution of a marriage, rather than adultery, a reason upon which numerous divorces were constructed during the 1920s when in many cases the adulterous liaison would be staged. Thus the Church took the guilt aspect out of divorce and paved the way for the so called 'no-blame' legislation of the 1960s. Divorce in England now, for adultery, intolerable behaviour, or desertion, or after a two-year period of separation and mutual consent, or after a five-year separation where there is no consent, is still undergoing changes. Many lawyers would like to see divorce become even easier.

Divorce, like marriage, varies from state to state in the USA, where people cross state lines or borders, to marry and divorce in a state with more flexible laws than their own.

SOLD FOR SIXPENCE

The idea that a wife could be sold should she no longer please her husband seems barbaric, but then so were many of the other practices in earlier centuries such as the sale of children, slaves and corpses. Nonetheless the practice of wife-selling existed until the 1880s in England – and it seems to have been a peculiarly English practice – where it was 'popularly believed to be a legal and valid form of divorce', according to Samuel Pyeatt Menefee in his book *Wives for Sale*. It was thought by many historians to date back to the Anglo-Saxons, although the first properly recorded case was as late as 1553.

In rural settings far away from the legal redress of larger towns people formed the habit or custom of their own laws. Thus England had myriad regional customs and laws, many of which were partially and inadequately recorded. Since divorce prior to 1857 required an act of Parliament and was not only expensive to achieve, but also required a knowledge of the law and substantial connections to steer the parties involved through the right channels, it was obviously beyond the hope of anyone but a member of the nobility. The poor man, the worker, therefore arranged his own laws to suit his needs, and after centuries these laws were accepted by the populace as being valid. Thus wife sales arose because of the desire of both parties to end a marriage, the difficulty in achieving a divorce and the absence of church law enforcement.

It has been suggested that wife sales occurred when either party had committed adultery and no longer wished to live with their spouse but with their new lover. Unable to do this without becoming social outcasts, the individuals arranged a 'sale' to rectify the situation, and to save face for the husband if he was in the position of cuckold, which would attract great ridicule from his friends and neighbours.

The custom of wife-selling involved bringing the wife, with a halter about her neck, to a public place such as a market hall or market cross, a fair or a 'hiring', when there would be numerous people about not only to bid, but also to witness and hence validate the transaction. Witnesses were essential to the deal in the event that a dispute between the parties followed. Many wife sales took place in inns or alehouses, which leads historians to the conclusion that these sales were alcohol-induced, the strong liquor inciting a daring that otherwise would not have been in evidence. In some cases it appears that wives were even sold for drink, and there was at least one case of a man expressing a preference for his bottle over his wife.

'HERE – I am waiting to know about this offer of mine. The woman is no good to me. Who'll have her?'

The company had by this time decidedly degenerated, and the renewed inquiry was received with a laugh of appreciation. The woman whispered; she was imploring and anxious: 'Come, come, it is getting dark, and this nonsense won't do. If you don't come along, I shall go without you. Come!'

She waited and waited; yet he did not move. In ten minutes the man broke in upon the desultory conversation of the furmity drinkers with, 'I asked this question, and nobody answered to 't. Will any Jack Rag or Tom Straw among ye buy my goods?'

The woman's manner changed, and her face assumed the grim shape and colour of which mention has been made.

'Mike, Mike,' said she; 'this is getting serious. O! – too serious!'

'Will anybody buy her?' said the man.

'I wish somebody would,' said she firmly. 'Her present owner is not at all to her liking!'

'Nor you to mine,' said he. 'So we are agreed about that. Gentlemen, you hear? It's an agreement to part. She shall take the girl if she wants to, and go her ways. I'll take my tools, and go my ways. 'Tis simple as Scripture history. Now then, stand up, Susan, and show yourself.'

'Don't, my chiel,' whispered a buxom staylace dealer in voluminous petticoats, who sat near the woman; 'yer good man don't know what he's saying.'

The woman, however, did stand up. 'Now who's auctioneer?' cried the hay-trusser.

'I be,' promptly answered a short man, with a nose resembling a copper knob, a damp voice, and eyes like button-holes.

'Who'll make an offer for this lady?'

The woman looked on the ground, as if she maintained her position by a supreme effort of will.

'Five shillings,' said some one, at which there was a laugh.

'No insults,' said the husband. 'Who'll say a guinea?'

Nobody answered; and the female dealer in staylaces interposed.

'Behave yerself moral, good man, for Heaven's love! Ah, what a cruelty is the poor soul married to! Bed and board is dear at some figure's, 'pon my 'vation 'tis!'

'Set it higher, auctioneer,' said the trusser.

'Two guineas!' said the auctioneer; and no one replied.

'If they don't take her for that, in ten seconds they'll have to give more,' said the husband. 'Very well. Now, auctioneer, add another.'

'Three guineas – going for three guineas!' said the rheumy man.

'No bid?' said the husband. 'Good Lord, why she's cost me fifty times the money, if a penny. Go on.'

'Four guineas!' cried the auctioneer.

'I'll tell ye what – I won't sell her for less than five,' said the husband, bringing down his fist so that the basins danced. 'I'll sell her for five guineas to any man that will pay me the money, and treat her well; and he shall have her for ever, and never hear aught o' me. But she shan't go for less. Now then – five guineas – and she's yours. Susan, you agree?'

She bowed her head with absolute indifference.

'Five guineas,' said the auctioneer, 'or she'll be withdrawn. Do anybody give it? The last time. Yes or no?'

'Yes,' said a voice from the doorway.

All eyes were turned. Standing in the triangular opening which formed the door of the tent was a sailor, who, unobserved by the rest, had arrived there within the last two or three minutes. A dead silence followed his affirmation.

'You say you do?' asked the husband, staring at him.

'I say so,' replied the sailor.

'Saying is one thing, and paying is another. Where's the money?'

The sailor hesitated a moment, looked anew at the woman, came in, unfolded five crisp pieces of paper, and threw them down upon the tablecloth. They were Bank-of-England notes for five pounds. Upon the face of this he chinked down the shillings severally – one, two, three, four, five.

The sight of real money in full amount, in answer to a challenge for the same till then deemed slightly hypothetical, had a great effect upon the spectators. Their eyes became riveted upon the faces of the chief actors, and then upon the notes as they lay, weighted by the shillings, on the table.

Up to this moment it could not positively have been asserted that the man, in spite of his tantalizing declaration, was really in earnest. The spectators had indeed taken the proceedings throughout as a piece of mirthful irony carried to extremes; and had assumed that, being out of work, he was, as a consequence, out of temper with the world, and society, and his nearest kin. But with the demand and response of real cash the jovial frivolity of the scene departed. A lurid colour seemed to fill the tent and change the aspect of all therein. The mirth-wrinkles left the listeners' faces, and they waited with parting lips.

'Now,' said the woman, breaking the silence, so that her low dry voice sounded quite loud, 'before you go further, Michael, listen to me. If you touch that money, I and this girl go with the man. Mind, it is a joke no longer.'

'A joke? Of course it is not a joke!' shouted her husband, his resentment rising at her suggestion. 'I take the money: the sailor takes you. That's plain enough. It has been done elsewhere – and why not here?'

''Tis quite on the understanding that the young woman is willing,' said the sailor blandly. 'I wouldn't hurt her feelings for the world.'

'Faith, nor I,' said her husband. 'But she is willing, provided she can have the child. She said so only the other day when I talked o't!'

'That you swear?' said the sailor to her.

'I do,' said she, after glancing at her husband's face and seeing no repentance there.

'Very well, she shall have the child, and the bargain's complete,' said the trusser. He took the sailor's notes and deliberately folded them, and put them with the shillings in a high remote pocket, with an air of finality.

The sailor looked at the woman and smiled. 'Come along!' he said kindly. 'The little one too – the more the merrier!' She paused for an instant, with a close glance at him. Then dropping her eyes again, and saying nothing, she took up the child and followed him as he made towards the door. On reaching it, she turned, and pulling off her wedding-ring, flung it across the booth in the hay-trusser's face.

Thomas Hardy, *The Mayor of Casterbridge*

Prior to a wife sale, bills were posted and advertisements placed in newspapers describing the wife who was to be sold. Some women were given the attributes of being 'smart', or 'very pretty and modest looking', while others were called 'disagreeable' or 'lazy'. One wonders, given modern advertising customs, why anyone would advertise the negative aspects of their goods for sale, but perhaps it has something to do with the fact that many of the wife sales, historians believe, were pre-arranged and that a current or potential lover would purchase the wife at a price that had been agreed upon beforehand with the husband. Thus the wife was described in derogatory terms to deter any potential buyer. The husband of the wife would hand the halter rope to his wife's new owner, symbolically transferring all his responsibilities and claims.

The prices fetched for wives were not high. Some brought no more than a gallon of beer or ale, others fetched anything from a few pennies or shillings to £5. Not everyone was in agreement with the business of wife-selling, many feeling that it was morally wrong. In such cases a mob gathered and were known to attack the parties involved or at least harrass them, chasing them and shouting at them to the accompaniment of rough music, a traditional method of a crowd of people showing disapproval by banging and clattering household and farm utensils.

The transactions were not always a success. Some husbands, when sober, regretted their actions, as did their wives. The purchasers often changed their minds or were unhappy enough to return the women to the auction block. The practice of wife-selling attracted increasing disapproval during the nineteenth century as the educated Victorian moralists took the working classes to task. When the establishment of a secular Divorce Court in 1857 in theory made divorce easier to obtain, wife-selling was no longer tolerated.

Nebuchadnezzar, the King of the Jews,
Sold his wife for a pair of shoes.
When the shoes began to wear
Nebuchadnezzar began to swear.

Children's rhyme

Account of the
SALE of a WIFE, by J. NASH,
IN THOMAS-STREET MARKET,
On the 29th of May, 1823

THIS day another of those disgraceful scenes which of late have so frequently annoyed the public markets in this country took place in St. Thomas's Market, in this city; a man (if he deserves the name) of the name of John Nash, a drover, residing in Rosemary-street, appeared there leading his wife in a halter, followed by a great concourse of spectators; when arrived opposite the Bell-yard, he publicly announced his intention of disposing of his better half by Public Auction, and stated that the biddings were then open; it was a long while before any one ventured to speak, at length a young man who thought it a pity to let her remain in the hands of her present owner, generously bid 6d.! In vain did the anxious seller look around for another bidding, no one could be found to advance one penny, and after extolling her qualities, and warranting her sound, and free from vice, he was obliged, rather than keep her, to let her go at that price. The lady appeared quite satisfied, but not so the purchaser, he soon repented of his bargain, and again offered her to sale, when being bid nine-pence, he readily accepted it, and handed the lady to her new purchaser, who, not liking the transfer, made off with her mother, but was soon taken by her purchaser, and claimed as his property, to this she would not consent but by order of a magistrate who dismissed the case. Nash, the husband, was obliged to make a precipitate retreat from the enraged populace.

Copy of Verses written on the Occasion:

COME all you kind husbands who have scolding wives,
Who thro' living together are tired of your lives,
If you cannot persuade her nor good natur'd make her
Place a rope round her neck & to market pray take her

Should any one bid, when she's offer'd for sale,
Let her go for a trifle lest she should get stale,
If six pence be offer'd, & that's all can be had,
Let her go for the same rather than keep a lot bad.

Come all jolly neighbours, come dance sing & play,
Away to the wedding where we intend to drink tea;
All the world assembles, the young and the old,
For to see this fair beauty, as we have been told.

Here's success to this couple to keep up the fun,
May bumpers go round at the birth of a son;
Long life to them both, and in peace & content
May their days and their nights for ever be spent.

Till Death Us Do Part
by Edmund Blair Leighton.

Dutiful Daughters

IT is one of the disadvantages of your sex that young women are seldom permitted to make their own choice.

The Marquis of Halifax, *Advice to a Daughter*, 1700

It is impossible to write about marriage without including the subject of the status of women and how it relates to marriage. A number of books have been written which deal in depth with the changes in the lives of women (social, legal, etc) and it would be difficult to encapsulate that material here without demeaning it in some way. But to look at the history of marriage without reflecting something of the lives of women in the past would be a blinkered view indeed.

The greatest changes in lives of women came during the nineteenth century, which might be viewed as a plateau, for nothing compares to the culmination of events that began in the late eighteenth century and continued on into the early twentieth century. Over the centuries the main issues for women were education and employment, divorce and child custody rights, property and the vote, and it was during the nineteenth century that the legislation passed in Parliament paved the way for the relative freedoms and equality experienced by the twentieth-century woman.

Today's society encourages and supports the notion of love and marriage as being compatible lifetime partners, rather than marriage and duty to one's spouse regardless of whether one loved him or not. Women's lives are more self-directed than ever before, and it is not easy to accept that women once allowed themselves to be the passive players in a game of financial and social wheelings and dealings, ultimately becoming the objects of transfer from one man to another – father or brother to husband – under mutually agreeable terms, upon which many of them had little or no influence. (The only passive role women play in marriage today is that of waiting to be asked, and a quick look at contemporary women's magazines will reveal that this is not always the case.) By today's standards marriage to a man one barely knows and therefore can hardly love seems preposterous, and suggests either some form of barbaric rite, an urgent desire for the title of Mrs, or a business arrangement which must involve a large sum of money.

From the earliest human times, before even the barest structure of marriage between man and woman existed, the first social bonds were between mother and child, and marriage, in whatever primitive form recognized as such today, was an arrangement which could be terminated at will by either party. In *The Lady,* written by Emily James Putnam in 1910, the author states:

by degrees the man took possession. Perhaps the ownership of the husband in the wife and the children, known as the patriarchal or proprietary family, was the result of a gradual shift from more or less peaceful savagery to the fighting-stage as involving wife-capture; and wife-capture in its turn made the domestic subordination of even the woman of the man's own group seem right and fitting to all concerned. Perhaps on the other hand the early woman was undone simply by the inevitable working of the maternal instinct. This led her to build a shelter for the child, to keep a fire, to experiment with vegetable foods that she might not have to leave her nest and range too far afield. The early home of the mother and child became attractive to the man. It was a fixed point where he knew he could find shelter and food. When maternity had gone so far as to make woman synonymous with both superior comfort and inferior physique, the man moved in and made himself master. At any rate by fair means or foul two great human institutions were apparently inaugerated together, proprietary marriage and the division of society into masters and servants.

But since then women have fared poorly. For centuries a female belonged to her father until she was married and then she belonged to her husband, who replaced her father as her master and head of the household. When patriarchy was at its height during the nineteenth century, a woman's father, then her husband, was also head of the household to the servants and relatives living in the house. Aristocrat or pauper or anywhere in between, until the late nineteenth century a woman had no rights over her estate, her income, or her children. This situation, which is unthinkable today, was tolerated for centuries because there existed no alternative for women without the power of a vote or financial resources, in a climate which was hostile to women who stepped out of their assigned places, first as daughters, then as wives and ultimately as mothers. In pre-Revolutionary France a husband, father or brother could request of the king a *lettre de cachet* which was all that was needed to lock up a disobedient wife, daughter or sister. But as historian Barbara Hanawalt writes in *The Ties That Bound,* 'That the male was given a dominant role over his wife in law, and over women in general through office holding, does not automatically imply that he used his additional powers arbitrarily or viciously.'

From the early Middle Ages, as each successive century turned, women gained increasing liberty from the parameters placed around them not only by their fathers, brothers and husbands, but also by their own mothers who had acquiesced to the demands of their male kinfolk and expected their daughters to do the same without question. Although history holds examples of exceptional women, in most circumstances they were someone's wife. Under the guise of wife to a wealthy man a

*From a young Woman, a Servant in London,
to her Parents, desiring their consent to marry.*

HONOURED Father and Mother, – I have sent this to inform you, that one Mr Wood, a young man, a cabinet-maker, has paid his addresses to me, and now offers me marriage. I told him I would do nothing without your consent, and therefore have sent this by William Jones, your neighbour, who called on me, and will inform you particularly of his circumstances.

The young man has been set up in business about two years, and is very regular and sober. Most people in the neighbourhood esteem him, and his business is daily increasing. I think I could live extremely happy with him, but do not choose to give him my promise, until I have first heard from you: whatever answer you send shall be obeyed by

Your affectionate daughter.

The Parents' Answer

DEAR Child, – We received your letter by Mr Jones, and the character he gives of the young man is so agreeable, that we have no objection to your marrying him: begging that you will seriously consider the duties of that important state, before it is too late to repent. Consider well with yourself, that according to your conduct to each other, you must either be happy or miserable as long as you live. There are many occurrences in life in which the best of men's tempers may be ruffled, on account of losses or disappointments; if your husband should at any time be so, endeavour to make him as easy as possible. Be careful of every thing he commits to your keeping, and never affect to appear superior to your station: for although your circumstances may be easy, yet, whilst in trade, you will find a continual want of money for different purposes. It is possible some of your more polite neighbours may despise you for a while, but they will be forced in the end to acknowledge, that your conduct was consistent with the duties of a married state. But above all, remember your duty to God, and then you may cheerfully look for a blessing on your honest endeavours. May God direct you in every thing for the best, is the sincere prayer of

Your loving father and mother.

woman might become head of a business empire, a property developer, architect or builder. But her earnings belonged to her husband. If she had some form of income, either from her investments, the sale of property or from her own efforts such as royalties from published works, she might never see the cash in her purse. By law her husband was entitled to keep the funds in his bank account and dispose of them as he chose. There were, of course, husbands who ignored the law and allowed their wives access to their own earnings. Based on petition, The Married Women's Property Bill was introduced in 1857, after falling at the first reading in Parliament, which went some way towards redressing the imbalance that existed.

Regarding her children a married woman had no legal rights. And if her husband did not specify in his will that he granted his wife guardianship of their sons and daughters, the children became wards of her father-in-law. In the rare cases of divorce a woman's children would be taken from her. The Duke and Duchess of Saxe-Coburg Saalfeld, parents of Ernest and Albert, who was later to become Queen Victoria's consort, divorced by mutual consent in 1824. The Duchess never saw her children again. In 1836 the Honourable Caroline Norton was accused by her husband of adultery with the Prime Minister Lord Melbourne. Norton subsequently divorced his wife and gained custody of their three children. Partly as a result of Caroline Norton's efforts as a lobbyist, the first Custody of Infants Act, passed in 1849, gave mothers limited access to their children.

The subjugation of women started at birth. That male children were preferable to female children is true in almost all societies. Male babies were even disguised and dressed as female babies in long dresses to fool the spirits who, it was felt, also favoured male children. As an exception the Romans appeared to have treated their daughters fairly well, but in most societies women have been viewed as liabilities, financial burdens for parents who would be expected

—— ○ ——

Victorian sentimentalism, seen here in *Sweethearts* by Walter Dendy Sadler.

Not all proposals were related to marriage. *The Proposition* by
Pio Ricci.

to provide dowries in order to persuade a member of the opposite sex to remove the
daughter from the family hearth.

There existed the necessity of marrying off daughters of child-bearing age as
quickly as possible, for if a girl should become pregnant the chances of a subsequent
marriage – the father of the child being unwilling to marry the girl or, by his absence,
unable – were rare. Daughters of the wealthy were kept under close scrutiny,
accompanied everywhere by chaperones, often in the form of dowager aunts and
cousins who knew of the dangers and temptations presented by young men.
Heiresses were kept at home, away from fortune hunters who would rush them off to
Gretna Green.

As well as being considered socially inferior women were thought of as being
physically and emotionally inferior. Hysteria was believed to be an illness peculiar to
females and caused by the movement of the uterus: while it wandered freely about the
body it caused, amongst other things, tears, laughter and loss of breath. As
child-bearers women were viewed with suspicion and after confinement a ritualistic
cleansing was forced upon them, a 'churching' of the mother before she was free to
go about in society again. Throughout Roman pagan history adultery was a crime for
women only; and the legerwite in medieval England was the fine for an unmarried

woman's 'fornication'. In Elizabethan times women were considered to be born without a soul, and since the earliest days of society, as we would recognize it, women have been expected to act in a manner which reflected their inner submissiveness, dressing with modesty and keeping their eyes downcast. An upper-class woman showed her breeding and refinement by being helpless and dependent. Until the eighteenth century many men thought that education and the pursuit of intelligence only increased a woman's chances of becoming insane.

Men concerned themselves with the moral purity of women. Chastity belts, which have been traced back to the time of the Crusades, were used to ensure the faithfulness of wives to their husbands. Although the public eventually viewed these contraptions as instruments of torture, chastity belts were still being sold in Paris in the eighteenth century. Virginity, while less highly prized by ordinary folk, was of great significance to the aristocracy under the patriarchal, primogenitural system of inheritance. A woman was acquired by a man as property to begin a new line of heirs and her husband expected her to be a virgin on their wedding night. A father could disinherit a daughter who lost her virginity because she had decreased in value in his eyes and those of her potential suitors. In his book *For Better, For Worse,* John R. Gillis wrote:

> By the early nineteenth century even the slightest degree of independence in sexual matters could render a middle-class woman unfit for marriage or society. The sexuality of a wife or daughter was presumed to belong to the husband or father. They could sue those who tampered with their 'property', and even rape was treated as an offence, not just against the woman but against patriarchy.

Until relatively recently in our history women married because there were few options in life to do anything else. No form of employment was open to a girl of the gentry or upper classes. The option of the convent was available – although many doors were closed when Henry VIII dissolved the religious houses in England between 1535 and 1540 – but because the convent often required a dowry this alternative did not exist for poor women. As Barbara Hanawalt writes:

> For peasant daughters even more than for the daughters of the nobility, marriage was the universal objective. The convent, open to noblewomen, was closed to peasant girls in feudal society, for whom the only practical alternatives to marriage were to remain on the family holding and work for the inheriting brother, to become a servant for another village family or in the lord's household, or to hire out as casual labour.

Work for women in service – washmaids, dairymaids, cooks or ladies' maids – involved long back-breaking hours for little pay. For agricultural labour women received half the pay of men, and work in the city fell into the categories of street selling. Prostitution was the other alternative, which many unmarried women turned to especially if they had a child to support.

It would be fair to say that parents and daughters looked upon marriage as a career

Stepping into a wedding gown and changing one life for another. *The Wedding Gown* by John Faed.

———————— ○ ————————

Wife and servant are the same,
But only differ in the name . . .
When she the word 'obey' has said,
And man by law supreme has made . . .
Fierce as an Eastern Province he grows
And all his innate rigor shows.
Then but to look, to laugh, or speak
Will the nuptial contract break.
Like mutes she signs alone must make,
And never any freedom take,
But still be governed by a nod
And fear her husband as her God.

Lady Mary Chudleigh, 1703

———————— ○ ————————

which provided the opportunities of bettering their social position by 'marrying up'. In the late nineteenth century and early twentieth century the 'dollar princesses' from America married into the British aristocracy, their fathers pouring thousands of dollars into maintaining England's fine old estates in exchange for a title for their daughters. The 1906 musical, *The Dollar Princess,* merely coined a phrase for what had been a transatlantic business arrangement for years: the trade of titles for dollars. By the First World War over four hundred American women had become princesses, duchesses, countesses, viscountesses, marchionesses, baronesses, ladies or the wives of knights and baronets. The dollars their fathers paid to their husbands helped keep many members of the British aristocracy from bankruptcy, preserve the great English ancestral homes, and maintain the men in the style to which they had become

——————— ———————

Good breeding, fashion, dancing, dressing, play
Are the accomplishments we should desire;
To write, to read, to think, or to enquire
Would cloud our beauty, and exhaust our time,
And interrupt the conquests of our prime;
Whilst the dull manage, of a servile house,
Is held by some, our utmost art, and utmost use.

Anne Finch, Countess of Winchelsea, *c.* 1690

——————— ———————

accustomed. Not all 'princesses' were willing. Consuelo Vanderbilt, the daughter of William Kissam and Alva Smith Vanderbilt Belmont, wanted to marry a New York bachelor, but her parents had contracted with the ninth Duke of Marlborough, who received upon his marriage $2,500,000 of stock in the Beech Creek Railway Company with an annual payment of 4 per cent, which enabled him to restore, repair and improve Blenheim Palace.

From earliest times women had been urged to further the power base and field of influence of their own family by making 'good' marriages, and although this was significantly less important in a non-feudal society, marriage still provided the occasion to increase social contacts, provide heirs for the family and endow lands on relatives and children. It was part of her cultural education to make a young girl understand that she was expected to find a suitable man and marry him. The southern belles of the nineteenth century resembled their earlier medieval sisters: where the latter were paraded at court until marriage confined them to a cold castle tower, the former were encouraged to be social butterflies, dancing their way from ball to ball, because marriage would plant a matron's cap firmly upon their heads on a cotton plantation miles from anywhere. Many women were practically and emotionally unprepared for marriage and their mothers told them nothing that could have eased the transition from daughter to wife. Nonetheless they received a great deal of advice from other quarters, where young women were urged to fulfil their duties as daughters by marrying and bearing children to secure the line of inheritances. Mrs Sarah Ellis, in her book *The Wives of England*, written in the 1860s, complained that girls were ill-equipped for marriage from an emotional point of view, and that they had no experience of economics, or of dealing with her husband's relations or the servants. On the subject of husbands she wrote:

> Men who have been thus educated by foolish and indulgent mothers; who have been placed at public schools, where the influence, the character and the very name of woman was a by-word for contempt; who have been afterwards associated with sisters who were capricious, ignorant and vain – such men are very unjustly blamed for being selfish, domineering and tyrannical to the other sex. In fact, how should they be otherwise.

Books such as this one stressed the importance of young women performing their wifely duties, and welcoming their man to a trouble-free warm hearth.

Although marriage under these circumstances would not appeal today, it is worth noting what women had to gain by marriage, and to consider the situation of the unmarried daughter, or spinster. Once married a woman would be able to run her own home – subject to the tastes and budgetary demands of her husband – and have children, although until this century childbirth was a life-threatening experience which millions of women must have dreaded. Free from parental restraint she was likely to enjoy greater equality in making decisions which affected not only herself but the upbringing of her children and the control of her finances. A married woman

The writer of a love letter must be prepared for his words to be seen by others than his intended. *The Love Letter* by Vittorio Reggianini.

was, at the very least, a manager of her own home and, if her husband was a wealthy man, a household full of servants. Although they were seen as inferior in society, women nonetheless held positions of power within the family structure, especially in the frequent absences of their husbands.

A spinster – a word which originally denoted a spinning woman but came to mean from the seventeenth century an unwed woman – remained at the home of her parents. Without question she held the lowest rank in the family hierarchy, for a widow would be likely to have her own financial means of independence. An

AFTER a mutual silence of some minutes, Harriet thus began again –

'I do so wonder, Miss Woodhouse, that you should not be married, or going to be married! so charming as you are!' –

Emma laughed, and replied.

'My being charming, Harriet, is not quite enough to induce me to marry; I must find other people charming – one other person at least. And I am not only, not going to be married, at present, but have very little intention of ever marrying at all.'

'Ah! – so you say; but I cannot believe it.'

'I must see somebody very superior to any one I have seen yet, to be tempted; Mr Elton, you know, (recollecting herself,) is out of the question: and I do *not* wish to see any such person. I would rather not be tempted. I cannot really change for the better. If I were to marry, I must expect to repent it.'

'Dear me! – it is so odd to hear a woman talk so!' –

'I have none of the usual inducements of women to marry. Were I to fall in love, indeed, it would be a different thing! but I never have been in love; it is not my way, or my nature; and I do not think I ever shall. And, without love, I am sure I should be a fool to change such a situation as mine. Fortune I do not want; employment I do not want; consequence I do not

want: I believe few married women are half as much mistress of their husband's house, a I am of Hartfield; and never, never could I expect to be so truly beloved and important; so always first and always right in any man's eyes as I am in my father's.'

'But then, to be an old maid at last, like Miss Bates!'

'That is as formidable an image as you could present, Harriet; and if I thought I should ever be like Miss Bates! so silly – so satisfied – so smiling – so prosing – so undistinguishing and unfastidious – and so apt to tell every thing relative to every body about me, I would marry to-morrow. But between *us*, I am convinced there never can be any likeness, except in being unmarried.'

'But still, you will be an old maid! and that's so dreadful!'

'Never mind, Harriet, I shall not be a poor old maid; and it is poverty only which makes celibacy contemptible to a generous public! A single woman, with a very narrow income, must be a ridiculous, disagreeable, old maid! the proper sport of boys and girls; but a single woman, of good fortune, is always respectable, and may be as sensible and pleasant as anybody else.'

Jane Austen, *Emma*

unmarried daughter was a social outcast, an embarrassment, and as a spinster she would become an old maid, still the subject of ridicule in Victorian times; although much earlier, in the 1630s, Lettice Cary, Lady Falkland, had addressed the problem of unwed women and suggested the establishment of an institution for unmarried and unmarriageable daughters which would no doubt provide women with a safe haven from the cruelty of their families, and provide their families with a place to dispose of their daughters.

An unmarried daughter was expected to stay at home where her virginity could be preserved. There was no kind of employment suitable for someone of her station in life, if she came from the gentry, and the limited education available to her was a way of keeping her occupied until she married. Once she was permitted an education she was expected to submerge her knowledge into domestic duties. In 1911 Emily Jane Puttnam wrote, 'A girl should not be too intelligent or too good or too highly differentiated in any direction. Like a ready-made garment she should be designed to fit the average man. She should have "just about as much religion as my William likes".'

The unmarried daughter lived at home and kept count of the glass and silver and china. She would be called upon to tend sick relatives or look after elderly parents. Through society's eyes she saw herself as inferior and a failure for not being able to live up to her parents' expectations or expand the family's fortunes in any significant way. Instead she represented a financial burden for her parents. An unmarried daughter had to be fed, clothed and accommodated. Her maid's wages had to be paid and her doctor's bills met. She was last on the budget for clothing, travel and luxuries, yet society demanded that she dress herself appropriately and it was prudent – if expensive – for her parents to send her to stay with relatives in the hopes that she might broaden her social circle and in so doing meet a husband.

♥

HOW could she 'comfort father and mother,' when her own heart ached with a ceaseless longing for her sister; how could she 'make the house cheerful,' when all its light and warmth and beauty seemed to have deserted it when Beth left the old home for the new; and where in all the world could she 'find some useful, happy work to do,' that would take the place of the loving service which had been its own reward? She tried in a blind, hopeless way to do her duty, secretly rebelling against it all the while, for it seemed unjust that her few joys should be lessened, her burdens made heavier, and life get harder and harder as she toiled along. Some people seemed to get all sunshine, and some all shadow; it was not fair, for she tried more than Amy to be good, but never got any reward, only disappointment, trouble, and hard work.

Poor Jo, these were dark days to her, for something like despair came over her when she thought of spending all her life in that quiet house, devoted to humdrum cares, a few small pleasures, and the duty that never seemed to grow any easier.

Louisa M. Alcott, *Good Wives*

♥

A COUNTRY NEW JIG

Simon

O Mine owne sweet heart,
*   and when wilt thou be true:*
Or when will the time come,
*   that I shall marry you,*
That I may giue you kisses,
*   one, two or three,*
More sweeter then the hunny,
*   that comes from the Bee.*

Susan

My Father is vnwilling
*   that I should marry thee,*
Yet I could wish in heart,
*   that so the same might be:*
For now me thinks thou seemest,
*   more louely vnto me:*
And fresher then the Blossomes,
*   that bloomes on the tree.*

Simon

But stay heere comes my Mother,
*   weele talke with her a word:*
I doubt not but some comfort,
*   to vs she may afford:*
If comfort she will give vs,
*   that we the same may see,*
Twill be sweeter then the hunny,
*   that comes from the Bee.*

Susan

O Mother we are going
*   my Father for to pray,*
That he will giue me his good will,
*   for long I cannot stay.*
A young man I haue chosen
*   a fitting match for me,*
More fayrer then the blossomes
*   that bloomes on the tree.*

Mother

Daughter thou art old enough
*   to be a wedded wife,*
You maydens are desirous
*   to lead a marryed life.*
Then my consent good daughter
*   shall to thy wishes be,*
For young thou art as blossomes
*   that bloome vpon the tree.*

Simon

Then mother you are willing
*   your daughter I shall haue:*
And Susan thou art welcome
*   Ile keepe thee fine and braue.*
And haue those wished blessings
*   bestowed vpon thee,*
More sweeter then the honey
*   that comes from the Bee.*

Susan

Yet Simon I am minded
*   to lead a merry life,*
And be as well maintained
*   as any Citie wife:*
And liue a gallant mistresse
*   of maidens that shall be*
More fayrer then the blossomes
*   that bloome vpon the tree.*

The Second part. To the same tune.

Simon

Thou shalt haue thy Caudles,
*   before thou dost arise:*
For churlishnesse breeds sicknesse
*   and danger therein lies.*
Young lasses must be cherisht
*   with sweets that dainty be,*
Farre sweeter then the honey
*   that commeth from the Bee.*

Father

Why how now daughter Susan
  doe you intend to marry?
Maydens in the old time
  did twenty winters tarry.
Now in the teenes no sooner
  but you a wife will be
And loose the sweetest blossome
  that bloomes vpon thy tree.

Susan

It is for my preferment
  good father say not nay,
For I haue found a husband kinde
  and louing euery way:
That still vnto my fancy
  will euermore agree,
Which is more sweet then honey
  that comes from the Bee.

Simon

Good father be not cruell,
  your daughter is mine owne:
Her mother hath consented
  and is to liking growne.
And if your selfe will giue then,
  her gentle hand to me,
Twill sweeter be then honey
  that comes from the Bee.

The Fisherman's Wooing by
Eugene von de Blaas.

Father

God giue thee joy deare Daughter,
  there is no reason I
Should hinder thy proceeding,
  and thou a mayden die:
And after to lead Apes in hell,
  as maidens doomed be:
That fairer are then blossomes
  that bloome vpon the tree

All together sing

You Maidens and Bachelors
  we hope will lose no time,
Which learne it by experience
  that youth is in the prime,
And dally in their hearts desire
  young married folkes to be
More sweeter then the blossomes
  that bloome vpon the tree.

The governess rarely married. She occupied a difficult place in the household, belonging neither in the servant's hall nor at her employer's table. *The Governess* by Richard Redgrave.

A dowry must be available to her if she was expected to make a good match. In 1648 Mary Verney, under the protection of her brother Sir Ralph Verney, whose lack of money resulted in poor dowries for several of his sisters, was willing to accept a match proposed to her when she was over twenty years old – a considerable age by seventeenth-century standards – which she would have refused at a younger age and in a more comfortable financial position. She wrote: 'I am very sensible of my condition and am willing to settle myself if I can for the better and my friends cannot condemn me for it for a little of my own is better than a great deal of another's.'

The spinster whose parents were dead could find herself the unwanted guest pushed from the household of one sibling to another. It was not until the eighteenth century that large numbers of these women became governesses, leading a lonely life somewhere in the middle of the house, too good for the servants hall but not good enough for the patron's table. By the nineteenth century single middle-class women were more visible outside the home. Once the nursing profession became more respectable in the late nineteenth century, women found careers in hospital work and graduates from the universities were able to find positions as inspectors within the Civil Service.

But none of this resulted in any real independence or freedom as we would think of it today. Even if a woman inherited money, it was inconceivable that as a single woman she would set up house by herself, unless she was a widow. Her necessity for a husband would be even greater, as she would have been inadequately trained to manage her own finances. Under the circumstances then, a husband was perhaps the best solution.

CHILDREN are so much the goods, the possessions of their parents, that they cannot, without a kind of theft, give away themselves without the allowance of those that have the right in them.

Richard Allestree, *The Whole Duty of Man*, 1663

A daughter's ultimate task was to acquiesce to her parents' decision on the man chosen for her to marry. Whatever her fancy, a daughter living in an arranged marriage society, typically that of the wealthier classes who had established the patriarchal – property – marriage system, was expected to bend to her parents' will and to marry whomsoever they choose as her husband. Many young people were kept ignorant of the identity of their intended until the parents had worked out the details of the match. The parents' primary concerns were not the feelings of the two parties, but the financial, political and social advantages which the marriage could bring to their respective families. History presents contradictory evidence as to the extent of arranged marriages. Some historians believe that the arranged marriage was largely a facet of literature and that in real life young people had a much greater say in whom they married. Others have pointed out that, while this was true of the poorer classes for whom independence from the family had been a way of life since puberty, it was not the case for the propertied classes. It is all relative: a woman receiving only two proposals of marriage by parties approved by her parents might reject the first but accept the second rather than face the iniquitous position of old maid.

Arranged marriage exists in a great many societies which take the view that marriage is far too important to be left to children – given that marriage in the past was largely to do with property and social connections and had nothing to do with love. It was not uncommon to find that a father had stipulated in his will to whom his daughter was to be married, especially if he had undertaken the initial negotiations. Alternatives were offered should terms not be agreed upon. An heiress could be disinherited under the terms of her father's will if she did not agree.

It was not uncommon for families to engage middlemen as negotiators in marriage contracts. Samuel Pepys was asked to arrange the terms of a match between Lord Sandwich's eldest daughter, Lady Jemima Montagu, and Philip, the eldest son of Sir George Carteret, Treasurer of the Navy. Pepys dealt with Dr Timothy Clarke, physician to the Court and also to the Commission for Sick and Wounded Seamen, who was asked to negotiate on behalf of Sir George Carteret. Pepys spoke first to Dr Clarke and then to Sir George, who accepted the initial idea. The bride came with a dowry of £5,000 and her father expected a jointure for her of £800 a year. Pepys spent about a month travelling between the two parties – the match agreed upon, there seemed to be a great deal of social protocol involved. Pepys spent a little time with the young man and speaking on the subject of love found him to be 'the most awkerd man I ever I met withal in my life as to that business'. The families socialized together in order to let the young people get to know each other. On the day of the wedding Pepys found the groom 'backward almost in his caresses as he was the first day', and the Lady Jemima 'mighty sad', but thought that it might be her 'gravity, in a little greater degree than usual'.

---❤---

For what is wedlock forced, but a hell,
An age of discord and continual strife?
Whereas the contrary bringest bliss
And is a pattern of celestial peace.

William Shakespeare, *Henry VI*

---❤---

A great number of arranged marriages were contracted when the bride and groom were minors, often before they were old enough to marry. In royal circles many betrothals took place, usually by proxy, and the girl would then be married at the age of twelve, and the boy at the age of fourteen. Charles II's favourite, the Duke of Monmouth, was married off at the age of fourteen to the wealthy twelve-year-old Countess of Buccleuch. The King granted him £8,000 a year from the export of white draperies and £6,000 a year from excise receipts and a proportion of the money due to the Crown from ship wrecks.

With marriages where either or both parties required stringent demands to be met, negotiations might take months. If a contract was not ensuing this was often interpreted as a sign of deficiency on the part of the bride. With royal marriages, negotiations often took years. In the seventeenth century discussions between England and Spain took place over the proposed match of Prince Charles and the Spanish Infanta. The terms included a large dowry of about £500,000, but the Spaniards expected the Infanta to be given freedom to worship at her own chapels and bring her own Roman Catholic priests from Spain. They also wanted all English Catholics to be granted freedom of worship, or the conversion of Prince Charles to Catholicism. The parties, susceptible to political reactions within their own countries, could not agree. Prince Charles himself accepted that he should marry whomsoever was chosen for him in his country's best interests; his own feelings were considered unimportant. The Infanta, on the other hand, preferred to go into a convent than marry a Protestant. Although the treaties were finally drawn up, and presents were

Marriage romanticised. *The Betrothal of the Maid of Orleans* by Pierre-Jean van der Ouderra.

exchanged, Charles returned to England with his own retinue, the Infanta staying in Spain until the papal dispensation – necessary for the marriage of a Catholic to a Protestant – arrived. On his way home Charles decided against the marriage and ordered the proxy to be nullified. Marriage negotiations had taken over eight years.

Arranged marriages between royal houses were transferable. Ferdinand of Naples was initially betrothed to Maria Johanna, eleventh child of the Empress Maria Theresa of Austria and the Emperor Francis I. When Maria Johanna died of smallpox, her sister Maria Josephina became the intended of the King of Naples. Unfortunately, Maria Josephina also died of smallpox and as the betrothal arrangements were well advanced her sister, the thirteenth child, Maria Caroline was sent to be Queen of Naples.

Negotiations on behalf of Maria Antonia Joseph Johanna, Archduchess of Austria and Lorraine (Marie Antoinette) and the Dauphin of France took fifteen years, during

'COME hither, child,' said the old Earl of Courtland to his daughter, as, in obedience to his summons, she entered his study; 'come hither, I say; I wish to have some serious conversation with you: so dismiss your dogs, shut the door, and sit down here.'

Lady Juliana rang for the footman to take Venus; bade Pluto be quiet, like a darling, under the sofa; and, taking Cupid in her arms, assured his Lordship he need fear no disturbance from the sweet creatures, and that she would be all attention to his commands – kissing her cherished pug as she spoke.

'You are now, I think, seventeen, Juliana,' said his Lordship in a solemn important tone.

'And a half, papa.'

'It is therefore time you should be thinking of establishing yourself in the world. Have you ever turned your thoughts that way?'

Lady Juliana cast down her beautiful eyes, and was silent.

'As I can give you no fortune,' continued the Earl, swelling with ill-suppressed importance, as he proceeded, 'you have perhaps no great pretensions to a very brilliant establishment.'

'Oh! none in the world, papa,' eagerly interrupted Lady Juliana; 'a mere competence with the man of my heart.'

'The man of a fiddlestick!' exclaimed Lord Courtland in a fury; 'what the devil have you to do with a heart, I should like to know? There's no talking to a young woman now about marriage, but she is all in a blaze about hearts, and darts, and – and – But hark ye, child, I'll suffer no daughter of mine to play the fool with her heart, indeed! She shall marry for the purpose for which matrimony was ordained amongst people of birth – that is, for the aggrandisement of her family, the extending of their political influence – for becoming, in short, the depository of their mutual interest. These are the only purposes for which persons of rank ever think of marriage. And pray, what has your heart to say to that?'

'Nothing, papa,' replied Lady Juliana in a faint dejected tone of voice. 'Have done, Cupid!' addressing her favourite, who was amusing himself in pulling and tearing the beautiful lace veil that partly shaded the head of his fair mistress.

'I thought not,' resumed the Earl in a triumphant tone – 'I thought not, indeed.' And as this victory over his daughter put him in unusual good humour, he condescended to sport a little with her curiosity.

'And pray, can this wonderful wise heart of yours inform you who it is you are going to obtain for a husband?'

Had Lady Juliana dared to utter the wishes of that heart she would have been at no loss for a reply; but she saw the necessity of dissimulation; and after naming such of her admirers as were most indifferent to her, she declared herself quite at a loss, and begged her father to put an end to her suspense.

'Now, what would you think of the Duke of L—?' asked the Earl in a voice of half-smothered exultation and delight.

'The Duke of L—!' repeated Lady Juliana, with a scream of horror and surprise; 'surely, papa, you cannot be serious? Why, he's red-haired and squints, and he's as old as you.'

'If he were as old as the devil, and as ugly too,' interrupted the enraged Earl, 'he should be your husband: and may I perish if you shall have any other!'

The youthful beauty burst into tears,

Before the Wedding by F. S. Journalev.

while her father traversed the apartment with an inflamed and wrathful visage.

'If it had been anybody but that odious Duke,' sobbed the lovely Juliana.

'If it had been anybody but that odious Duke!' repeated the Earl, mimicking her, 'they should not have had you. It has been my sole study, ever since I saw your brother settled, to bring about this alliance; and, when this is accomplished, my utmost ambition will be satisfied. So no more whining – the affair is settled; and all that remains for you to do is to study to make yourself agreeable to his Grace, and to sign the settlements. No such mighty sacrifice, methinks, when repaid with a ducal coronet, the most splendid jewels, the finest equipages, and the largest jointure of any woman in England.'

Lady Juliana raised her head, and wiped her eyes. Lord Courtland perceived the effect his eloquence had produced upon the childish fancy of his daughter, and continued to expatiate upon the splendid joys that awaited her in a union with a nobleman of the Duke's rank and fortune; till at length, dazzled, if not convinced, she declared herself 'satisfied that it was her duty to marry whoever papa pleased; but –' and a sigh escaped her as she contrasted her noble suitor with her handsome lover: 'but if I should marry him, papa, I am sure I shall never be able to love him.'

The Earl smiled at her childish simplicity as he assured her that was not at all necessary; that love was now entirely confined to the *canaille*; that it was very well for ploughmen and dairymaids to marry for love; but for a young woman of rank to think of such a thing was plebeian in the extreme!

Susan Ferrier, *Marriage*

which time neither was consulted.

Although most royal marriages were arranged – from birth Princess Victoria of Kent was destined to marry Albert of Saxe-Coburg Saalfeld but it was coincidence that they loved each other – not all marriages between the nobility were arranged. Marie de Rabutin-Chantal, Madame de Sévigné, was married off to Henri, Marquis de Sévigné in

> *Oh, how fatal are forc'd marriages!*
> *How many Ruins one such Match pulls on!*
> *Had I bet kept my sacred vows to Gayman,*
> *How happy had I been – how prosperous he!*
> *Whilst now I languish in a loath'd embrace,*
> *Pine out my Life with Age – Consumption, Coughs.*
>
> Aphra Behn, *The Lucky Chance*, 1686

1644, an arranged marriage common enough at the time. Her daughter, however, refused several potential suitors, and when she did marry in 1668, her mother had great difficulty in accepting that her daughter's marriage was actually a love match.

Some daughters were able to persuade their parents to accept the man of their choice rather than a husband selected for them, but orphan heiresses were never so fortunate. Through no design of their own, some girls became substantial heiresses, there being no male heir alive to inherit. When the parents of these girls died prematurely without arranging a suitable marriage, the wardship of the girl was given to a male relative, or to the king who, unwilling to have his household full of wards, would sell the wardships to interested parties. These parties were often parents, men who wished to purchase an heiress for their son, or, in some cases, for themselves.

Charles Brandon, Duke of Suffolk, bought from the king the wardship of Catherine Willoughby whom he married in 1533, three months after his wife had died. Catherine was seventeen, the Duke of Suffolk forty-seven. By marriage she became, after royalty, the second highest-ranking duchess in the country, which must have made her subsequent marriage, after the death of the Duke, to Richard Bertie, a member of her household, extraordinary to the extreme.

Orphaned girls of good families with inheritances were caught in the crossfire of family battles. The male members of the families wanted these girls for their sons, while others wanted to see the girls locked away in convents so that their fortunes could be appropriated. In 1625 at the age of nine, Mary Blacknall lost both parents in the plague. Three years later, when she was living under the jurisdiction of the Court of Wards, Sir Edmund Verney became interested in her as a bride for his son, Ralph. Mary's relatives tried unsuccessfully to prevent Sir Edmund from acquiring her, but in 1629 the Court of Wards accepted £1,000 for Mary and she was married off to Ralph Verney. For the city of London female orphan heiresses were a source of revenue: as the property of the city these girls were sold off in marriage by the Courts of Wards, the wealthiest orphans bringing in the largest fees. This practice was abolished during the Restoration.

Another ward of the City of London was Sara Cox. In 1637, aged fourteen, while attending school she was abducted by the brother of a fellow student who had heard of her inheritance. Roger Fulwood carried her off to the house of the Bishop of Winchester where his mother, Lady Fulwood, waited to lure the young girl into the chapel. Sara Cox was forcibly married to Roger Fulwood and placed in bed with her new husband to consummate the marriage. She was rescued by officers of the law and Roger Fulwood was imprisoned. His release was secured only when he agreed to a suit of nullity of the marriage, thus freeing Sara from him.

Abduction, originally a German practice, was not uncommon, especially in the Middle Ages. After her marriage to Louis VI had been annulled, Eleanor of Aquitaine travelled to her palace of Maubergeon at Poitiers. Her journey was fraught with the threat of abduction by the seventeen-year-old Geoffrey of Anjou, younger brother of Henry, Duke of Normandy, who lay in ambush for her along the road. She successfully avoided him but must have realized the necessity for a swift remarriage if she did not want to be taken by force. Eight weeks after the annulment of her first marriage she married Henry, Duke of Normandy.

Abduction continued to be practised in England for several centuries despite statutes passed under Henry VII, Queen Mary and Queen Elizabeth I. During the Middle Ages it seemed that women went to great lengths to avoid forced marriages and to protect their virginity. Saint Gertrude, the first abbess of Nivelles, tonsured her daughter in order to disguise her from invading soldiers. Some women went so far as to mutilate themselves so that their intended husbands would no longer find them appealing.

Another solution was to elope with someone. One might think that elopements were the stuff of fiction were it not for the evidence of the business transacted at Gretna Green and at the Fleet in London where numerous weddings were transacted in the seventeenth century.

Writers such as Shakespeare, Tolstoy, Dickens and Jane Austen have included elopements in their works. In real life, elopements were often between an impoverished man and a wealthy heiress and occurred when the girl's father had rejected the suit of the

From a young Gentleman, in expectation of an estate from his penurious Uncle, to a young Lady of small fortune, desiring her to elope with him to Scotland.

MY dear Maria, – My uncle's laying his injunctions upon me to see you no more has only served to add fuel to my passion. I cannot live without you, and if you persist in refusing to comply, I am miserable for ever. I pay no regard to his threatenings, when put in competition with the love I have for you. Don't be afraid of poverty: if he should continue inexorable, I have still education sufficient to procure a genteel employment in one of the public offices, where I may rise to preferment. Therefore, if ever you loved me, let me beg that you will not make me any longer unhappy. Let me entreat you by all that's dear, that you will comply with my request, and meet me at six on Sunday evening, at the back door of the garden, where a chaise and four will be ready. I will fly on the wings of love to meet my charmer, and be happy in her embraces for ever. – I am, your dear lover.

Fleet weddings attracted those who married without parental consent or approval.

man, such as the case in the sixteenth century of the younger son of the first Earl of Rutland, who was considered unsuitable for Dorothy Vernon, the daughter of the owner of Haddon Hall. In the eighteenth century Bessie Surtees, daughter of a wealthy family, ran off with a poor tutor who subsequently became both wealthy and respected. In the following century, Jane Ward, a twelve-year-old heiress, ran off with her music teacher.

In other cases, otherwise happily married men were smitten by young girls and eloped with them to Europe were they remained in order to avoid prosecution in England for bigamy. Wealthy members of the aristocracy who chose to elope – even if neither party were married – often had to live abroad afterwards: on home turf they would have been ostracized by society.

Perhaps one of the most famous elopements was that of Lady Mary Pierrepoint, who eloped with Edward Wortley Montagu, after Montagu's suit had been refused by Mary's father. The couple lived abroad and in 1715 Montagu was appointed Minister Plenipoteniary to the Porte at the Sultan's court in Constantinople.

So far this chapter has dealt with aspects of marriage for the wealthy. For poor girls, without a dowry to attract an eligible suitor, the proposition of marriage was completely different. It would be hard to impose restrictions upon a girl who, from the age of twelve, had been completely independent from her family. There is some evidence to suggest that young women actively sought independence from their families and even their villages. If they could avoid getting pregnant, and therefore losing their jobs, they were often able to save up a little money with which to attract a man. Unfortunately, once they were in a position to be self-sufficient – and if their employer would tolerate married servants – they often discovered that men wanted younger wives.

Many historians have tried to discover at what age young people married and whether they made their own choices or not. The manorial court rolls of the Middle Ages have yielded information regarding the merchet, which was a fine paid to the lord of a manor by his vassals, a combination of land tax and marriage fee. It was seen as compensation for the vassal whose services the lord would lose when the vassal married into another manor. In about one third of the cases, the merchet was paid by the woman herself, which suggests to historians that she had free choice in the matter of selecting a husband.

The ages for consent for young men and women – at ages twelve to fifteen in the various law codes throughout the Middle Ages – implies, amongst other things, that boys and girls were free to choose their own spouses. However, teenage couples would have no economic means of support and they would be forced to ask for parental approval and the loan or gift of money with which to embark upon marriage.

Although the Church stressed freedom of choice for both parties in marriage, it seems that prior to the nineteenth century marriages of all classes, except the very poor who had nothing to lose or gain from the match, were arranged by parents, or by the young people themselves with the consent of their parents and friends. Obtaining the consent of friends and relatives was an important aspect of marriage which has been lost to us. Relatives and friends who approved of the match could provide support in a financial manner as well as good connections. For a young

---

PERHAPS there is nothing that is more annoying to the average woman who wishes to marry a particular man than to see him carried off by some other woman – unless not getting married at all be more annoying to a woman than the failure to marry the man she fancies.

No one can doubt that there are many most pleasant spinsters, no longer in the first bloom of youth, who would make excellent wives, and one has often been surprised to see such women left unmarried, while other women, in no respect superior to these pleasant spinsters, are often married.

This and other things I have noticed cause me to think there has been, and still is, a great misdirection of energy on the part of spinsters who wish to marry. While there is much that is unpalatable to the average man in women who are too obviously bent on marriage, there is surely no reason why a thoroughly nice woman who prefers matrimony to a single life should not, within the limits of good taste and of discretion, direct her attractiveness into the channel that is the most likely to aid her in attaining her desire; but this is seldom done, or, if done sometimes by chance or by intuition, this right direction, by a woman, of her endeavour to marry, is not carried out with any clear idea as to who is the most likely man to marry her.

John Holt Schooling, *A Woman's Chance of Marriage*

Families pursued couples who eloped across England to the Scottish border. *The Elopement Discovered* by Alexander Rosell.

couple to marry without consent would most likely result in isolation from the community. Certainly, a young woman who married against her parents' wishes would jeopardize any kind of dowry she was expecting to take with her to the marriage, and therefore she was unlikely to receive any kind of jointure.

When the notion that women might have some say in the matter began to be entertained from the late eighteenth century and during the nineteenth century, women were urged to consider carefully the kind of men they chose for husbands – even within the limited framework of arranged matches because, according to Dr C. W. Saleeby, writing in the early twentieth century, they were choosing the 'fathers of the future'.

Every woman must admit to curiosity about the man she might marry – today no less than yesterday. Who will he be and when will she be married? Some women even wished to know how many husbands they would have, as in medieval times it was not uncommon for a woman to be married to an older man, widowed early in her marriage and then to marry again, only this time she would select a younger man.

———————— ————————

IN order to be happy, a woman needs only a good digestion, a satisfactory complexion, and a lover. The first requirement being met, the second is not difficult to obtain, and the third follows as a matter of course.

Myrtle Reed, *The Spinster Book*, 1903

———————— ♡ ————————

Old customs directed a young girl to look in the fire on Christmas Eve if she wanted to see a glimpse of her future husband or to stand, at Halloween, in front of a mirror and brush her hair three times. If the image of a man appeared over her shoulder she would be married within the year. To dream of their husbands girls were instructed to put daisy roots under their pillows at night.

Gypsies searched for the mule with the longest ears in the gypsy encampment and whispered a question into its ears pertaining to the identity of the bridegroom. If the animal shook its head, the gypsy would assume that she would be a bride within a year. If the mule only moved an ear, the question of the wedding would not be answered soon, while if there was no movement at all from the mule, the gypsy would remain a spinster for that year.

One could use nuts to divine the identity of a future spouse. Laying a nut in the hot embers of the fire a girl would say the name of the man she loved. If the nut jumped away the couple would marry; if the nut did not move the relationship would be unsuccessful.

The patron saint of spinsters, St Catherine used to be appealed to on 25 November when young girls chanted the following rhyme:

> *A husband, St Catherine;*
> *A handsome one, St Catherine;*
> *A rich one, St Catherine;*
> *A nice one, St Catherine;*
> *And soon, St Catherine.*

On St Andrew's Day, celebrated on 30 November, young German girls stripped themselves naked and asked St Andrew for an affectionate husband and an indication of what kind of man he might be.

January the twenty-first is St Agnes' Eve and custom had it that a girl wishing to know her future husband had to go to bed supperless, or fast from midnight on 20 January to midnight 21 January. There are several St Agnes' Eve rituals; one has the girl taking a row of pins and, pulling every one out, she must say a Pater Noster and stick each pin into her sleeve. Another charm for St Agnes' Eve was to take a sprig of rosemary and a sprig of thyme and sprinkle them three times with water. Each sprig was placed in a shoe, the pair of shoes then being placed on each side of the bed and a rhyme repeated:

> *St Agnes, that's to lovers kind,*
> *Come ease the trouble of my mind.*

Yet another St Agnes' Eve ritual was for a girl to go to bed by herself, neither speaking nor looking to the right or left or behind her. Lying on her left side she was supposed to recite three times:

> *Saint Agnes be a friend to me,*
> *In the gift I ask of thee,*
> *Let me in this night my husband see.*

If a girl spent the night in a house other than her own on St Agnes' Eve she should take her right leg stocking and, knitting the left leg garter around it, repeat:

> *I knit this, this knot I knit,*
> *To know the thing I know not yet,*
> *That I may see*
> *The man that shall my husband be,*
> *Not in his best or worst array,*
> *But what he weareth every day;*
> *That I tomorrow may him ken*
> *From amongst all other men.*

After reciting this she was supposed to lie down on her back with her hands under her head and dream of her future husband.

October the sixth was known as St Faith's Day, when a cake of flour, sugar and salt was baked in strict silence by three girls who, during the baking process, each turned the cake three times. When the cake was ready it was divided into equal parts and each girl then cut her piece into nine pieces which she threaded through a wedding ring borrowed from a woman who had been married for seven years. When the girls retired to one bed the ring was hung by string at the head of the bed. Before falling asleep the girls recited in unison:

> *O good St Faith, be kind tonight,*
> *And bring to me my heart's delight;*
> *Let me my future husband view*
> *And be my visions chaste and true.*

A man's occupation was important as it would reflect upon the style and manner in which a woman would live the rest of her life, hence just one version of the children's rhyme:

> *Tinker, tailor,*
> *Soldier, sailor,*
> *Rich man, poor man,*
> *Beggar man, thief.*

According to folklore, sighting any of the following birds on St Valentine's Day would give a clear indication to a girl as to the occupation or disposition of her husband-to-be:

blackbird	=	a member of the Church
bluebird	=	a poor man
bluetit	=	a happy man
crossbill	=	an argumentative man
dove	=	a fortunate man
goldfinch	=	a rich man
robin redbreast	=	a sailor
sparrow	=	a humble man
yellowbird	=	a modestly wealthy man
woodpecker	=	no man
wryneck	=	no marriage

Presumably, if she knew a man whose profession was one of the above she would be inclined to look upon him expectantly with a view to a potential match.

THOUGHTS FOR GIRLS ABOUT TO MARRY

The Analyst
It would be trying, I insist,
To wed a Psycho-Analyst,
Were you attached to your relations
He'd warn you of quite odd temptations,
While if you thought them horrid bores
He'd mention complexes by scores,
And as for love, he'd sniff – 'Oh, no!
You've nothing but a Libido!'

The Mortician
And yet – just think of your position
If you should marry a Mortician!
If you should give a friend a pie
She'd think she was about to die;
If you asked 'How is Bill today?'
She'd glare at you and walk away
And think, no matter what your aims,
'She's hunting business for her James!'

The Iceman
But even less it would be nice
To take the man who sells the ice;
When you were dying with the heat
He'd grin and feel that life was sweet,
While if it turned the least bit cold
He'd sit at home and sulk and scold
And people would give leering looks
And make quite vulgar jokes on Cooks.

The Millionaire
In fact, dear child, to be quite fair
I would advise a Millionaire.

Margaret Widdemer

Merry Widows

In his book *Advice to Young Men, 1837, and (incidentally) to Young Women in the Middle and Higher Ranks of Life*, William Cobbett tackled the subject of a husband's attitude to his young wife and reminds him that 'the first frown she receives from you is a dagger to her heart'. He continues: 'As to oldish ones, or widows, time and other things have, in most cases, blunted their feelings, and rendered harsh or stern demeanour in the husband a matter not of heart-breaking consequence.'

It would be truthful to say that the reputation of the widow in English history, and particularly in the Middle Ages, was somewhat tarnished. From the early medieval period we are given the impression that widows in the peasantry were viewed as poor, defenceless creatures; some were considered subjects of the devil or even witches themselves. Examples from literature for the later Middle Ages often portray widows as penurious, greedy and even lusty, with an unquenchable thirst for chasing young men. Under medieval law a widow who had sexual relations with a man was treated as an adulteress and she was tried by the ecclesiastical courts. She would be fined by the manor court where she lived, or her lands would be forfeited temporarily. In extreme cases she would forfeit her dower – the third of her husband's estate to which she was entitled by common law.

> *Young maidens are bashful, but widows are bold*
> *They tempt poor young men with their silver and gold*
> *For love nowadays for money is sold*
> *If she be worth a treasure no matter how old.*

> Martin Parker, *c.*1625

How the widow's reputation came to be thus sullied is hard to determine, but it could well have something to do with the fact that when a woman became a widow she was technically free for the very first time in her life. No longer was she under the jurisdiction of her father, or her husband, and this single, self-supporting state could be conceived as quite threatening in a world where men were brought up to expect the dependency and deference of their daughters and wives. In addition, a widow had control of the money and lands that she was entitled to by law from her husband's estate. If she chose not to remarry and lived a long time, she could deprive her eldest son of his inheritance. If she decided to remarry she would have a certain amount of choice in the matter of selecting her husband, something that may well have been denied to her for her first marriage.

Women in the past tended to outlive their husbands, just as they do today. Historian Barbara Hanawalt writes in her book *The Ties that Bound,*

> the death of the husband brought a variety of new options and new independence, both economically and emotionally, that women could not achieve in any other phase of their life cycle. Widows were thrust into a new position, legally and personally, which gave them a greater role in planning their own future and that of their children. A widow could enter into land contracts on her own, could decide on marriage alliances for her children, could make her own decisions about remarriage and who she would marry. The new-found freedom, however, was not welcomed by all widows; some flourished and others suffered.

In the arranged-marriage society that existed until the nineteenth century, the father of the groom provided a jointure, which was an annual allowance or piece of land (which could be sold) for the bride in the event of her widowhood. If it was a monetary gift, it was often calculated as being one tenth of the size of the dowry brought to the marriage by the bride. The jointure was considered by some historians to be unnecessary because by customary law, confirmed by the Magna Carta in 1215, a third of the husband's estate was given to the wife on his death. From evidence found in the manorial court rolls of the Middle Ages and in wills of the period, it seems that husbands tended to be more generous. Historians examining these documents have come to the conclusion that the wife of a peasant in the Middle Ages was in fact a valued partner in what must resemble to us today more of a business relationship than a marriage. The wife's contribution to the domestic economy, and her worth in the eyes of her husband, were such that a man would often bequeath her his entire estate, putting in trust the portion due to his children and leaving to his widow's judgement the size of the settlements to be made on his sons, and of the dowries for his daughters. Many widows were appointed executors of their husbands' wills.

In some cases the widow would be given the usufruct of the property for her lifetime, or until the eldest son reached his majority – which was usually at twenty-one years of age. It was not uncommon for a husband to decree that his wife should have the use of certain lands and possessions until she remarried, when the land would become the property of the eldest son. The lands referred to in the will usually indicated family land.

Following the sentiments already expressed in wills of the period, during the fourteenth century a new form of marriage contract emerged which pledged joint tenancy of the land by husband and wife during their lifetime. After the

Hogarth's comment on marriage: *Marriage à la Mode: The Contract.*

death of one party, the other would be entitled to the estate – which was an improvement on the traditional women's third share. Thus a widow could become sufficiently wealthy on the death of her husband to remain single for the rest of her life. She could call upon brothers, sons and uncles to assist her with her financial transactions and should she fall upon hard times she could always let rooms in her home, run a tavern or take in washing – the traditional services that poor widows offered society.

But the advantages of widowhood were evidently not great enough to prevent women from remarriage and relinquishing their right to live beyond the authoritative arm of the male. In choosing to remarry, a widow's reasoning would be completely different from what it would be today. From a current viewpoint the widow's lot was far preferable to that of a daughter, with the prospect of an unwanted marriage ahead, or that of a wife, who was bound to honour and obey a man she didn't love for the rest of her life. However, a widow left in a man's world with a man's business to run – especially if she was untrained in business matters – or lands to cultivate and a home to manage, possibly with young children, might look favourably on another man who could be a father to her children and help with the family business – even though wives of guild members were entitled to the same rights as their deceased husbands. In the absence of a husband widows were obliged to hire labourers to work the fields and the services of other men to fulfil their obligations to the lord of the manor. For this reason, a widow often selected as a second husband a former business associate of her husband's, or even an apprentice, someone who had knowledge of her business. In such cases it was not uncommon for a man to assume the widow's surname. (In medieval Italy, when the local populace wished to show its disapproval of a widow's remarriage, particularly if she had taken a younger man as her husband, there developed a custom known as the *charivari*: a noise-making group of people who banged and clattered household and agricultural implements under the widow's bedroom on her wedding night.)

On the other hand a second marriage could result in an additional family, which would threaten the widow's first family; and while remarriage might improve the family status by joining together lands and holdings with those owned by the new husband, it could create disputes over property from families on both sides when either the widow or her second husband died.

Many women of the nobility chose to remain single to protect their children from the custodial rights of a new husband who could, if he chose, disinherit her son in favour of his own or of a son born from the new marriage. Given the sentiment of the times, it would be foolish to imagine that pressure was not brought upon widows within the family unit to marry a man whose own wealth and status would greatly enhance that of the widow's family.

Until about the middle of the fourteenth century widows were in demand, not only for the dowries they brought with them but also for their experience as housewives, social companions and lovers. Widows were particularly attractive to younger men, who were able to exchange youth and labour for a share of the widow's land when she died, especially men who did not intend to have a large family. Judging by the material available from the period, the marriage of an elderly widow to a younger man was not at all uncommon.

After the Black Death, however, the problem of land shortage was temporarily resolved, increasing the availability of land to an extent that widows were no longer so attractive as marriage partners.

In theory, widows were entitled to marry whomsoever they pleased, but under the feudal system they were obliged to notify the lord who was interested in the marriages of his tenants, particularly in the kind of man a widow married, because the lord was dependent on that man for his rents and services due.

In most cases the lord was unlikely to interfere in marriages of the peasantry, but amongst the nobility the remarriage of widows was of much greater consequence. The union of two families might create a stronghold of land and power that a lord, or even the king, might find a potential threat. Rarely were widows permitted to accumulate great lands and wealth and hold them in their own names. They might be coerced into parting with property in favour of a son, only to live quietly somewhere until they died. Certain convents accepted widows who had a sufficient dowry for admittance.

When a man died prematurely his wife was left to provide for the child with no obvious means of support.

Widows of the nobility were sometimes viewed as tools to further the aims of ambitious men. Antonia Fraser cites in her book *The Weaker Vessel* the case of Hawisa, Countess of Aumale, and widow of the Earl of Essex, who was married off to William de Forz, a man of lower social standing than herself, by Richard I who threatened to seize her possessions should she not comply. In the thirteenth century, the Magna Carta improved the lot of widows, stating that widows should not be forced to remarry.

Some widows had a strong sense of self-preservation. When Sir William Cavendish died in 1557 he left his widow, Elizabeth Hardwick, or Bess as she was known, with six children and debts to the Crown of £5,000. The following year when Queen Elizabeth ascended the throne, Bess became Lady of the Privy Chamber, and swiftly married Sir William St Loe, whose influence resulted in her paying off only £1,000 of her debts. When Sir William died six years later he left Bess his property and she now became a wealthy widow who could easily afford not to marry again, or to marry whomsoever she pleased. It took her three years to settle on George Talbot, the Earl of Shrewsbury, who was himself a widower with children and a very wealthy man. Under the terms of the marriage contract Bess arranged for her eldest son Henry to marry the earl's daughter Grace, and her youngest daughter, Mary, to marry the earl's second son Gilbert.

In the seventeenth and eighteenth centuries a wealthy widow or a widow of the nobility, if she was elderly or was able to resist family pressure to remarry, might enjoy a certain amount of freedom, living independently as a dowager, enjoying a limited social life, playing the role of chaperone to her granddaughters and nieces, and matchmaker for all her relatives. Madame de Sévigné was one such widow. Of course, the dowager's role was not as prestigious as that of a wife, but infinitely preferable to that of a spinster. Financial independence afforded widows a certain amount of respect, and no doubt the attention of a number of younger suitors.

The wealthy widow who found herself the owner of property or land upon the death of her husband was in a completely different situation from the poor widow who might find herself in strained financial circumstances with small children and no means by which to support them. Her family would be unlikely to accept her back and she would not be a welcome guest with the family of her deceased husband. Many poor widows found themselves in the workhouse, but it was not until the nineteenth century, with the moral concern of the Victorians with 'fallen women' that society shared any interest in them. As late as 1915 the Women's Industrial Council reported that:

> The widows are in worse case even than the wives, for they are often engaged at a low class of work without any previous training. The plight of such a woman – and there are many of them – is deplorable, for, if left with dependants, she must take whatever offers or starve. Of course there is always 'the House', but it is marvellous how the poor help one another in order to keep the home up, however humble it may be. . . . a number of widows marry again mainly that their young children may be looked after. Even an unemployed husband will keep toddling children from being run over, tumbling downstairs or setting themselves on fire.

It would be true to say that in the Middle Ages and in the following centuries when marriages made for convenience were the custom, a widow, who may not have been emotionally attached to her first husband, would have no compunction about marrying again. As illustrated above, there were certain advantages, not least the opportunity of a full social life from which a widow would be excluded. But from the late nineteenth century until the early twentieth century when there was a distinct swing to marriages made for love, a bereaved widow would not be in such a hurry to remarry. In fact, society, expecting to witness long years of mourning, viewed the swift remarriage of widows with horror. This attitude was set by Queen Victoria, who was widowed in 1861. She continued to wear black for years, stimulating business for the drapers and haberdashers who sold quantities of black crêpe, and setting new standards for mourning procedures.

It would also be true to say that women born in the first part of this century would find the idea of remarriage after being widowed socially and emotionally more difficult than women born in the second half of the twentieth century. Now, when divorce breaks up half as many marriages made, society does not expect long years of mourning for the loss of a partner, and it is more accepting of single women, be they unmarried, divorced or widowed.

> ON first thought, only two dates stand out in my mind: the date of the year of my birth and the date of the year of my marriage. But on second thought, I prefer to forget the year of my birth . . . the thought of my age depresses and dismays me. In its place, I am substituting the year of my widowhood which was calm and happy enough, a blessedly uneventful year, free of notoriety, out of the public eye.
>
> Madame de Sévigné

A Bachelor's Life

A married man is a man with a past, while
a bachelor is a man with a future.

George Bernard Shaw

Although women might dream about their future husbands, men, so we are to believe, took a different view of marriage. Many saw it as a practical and necessary step in the course of life. For a farmer or trader it made sense to marry and have someone to maintain his home, repair his clothes, feed him when he came home from work and, on occasion, provide another pair of hands in the field or shop-front. A wife, many believed, would provide the companionship that it was not possible to obtain from a servant. Others felt that marriage was inevitable but showed little enthusiasm: they feared the lack of freedom that marriage entailed and, worse, they were frightened of ending up with a scold or an ugly wife whom they would be obliged to feed, clothe and shelter. Others were determined to avoid marriage at all costs. Love, for the most part, seemed to feature hardly at all.

———————— ⬭ ————————

When roses grow on thistle tops,
And brimstone's took for sugar candy,
And women can't eat sugar sops,
Oh, then my love and I'll be married.

When a cobbler works without an awl,
And London into York is carried,
When smoke won't rise, nor water fall,
Oh, then my love and I'll be married.

Folk Songs of the Upper Thames, 1923

———————— ⬭ ————————

If a woman accepted that her husband was likely to be someone chosen, or at least introduced to her, by her parents, her expectations seemed to run along the lines of hoping that the man in question would be kind to her and their children. Men, on the

———— 78 ————

Royalty were seldom able to marry whom they pleased, rather the person chosen for them; although nineteenth-century painter Thomas Reynolds Lamont would have us believe otherwise in *The Prince's Choice.*

other hand, appeared to demand a great deal more from their wives. A lack of documentation prevents us from really knowing the motivation behind marriage prior to the late Middle Ages and it is therefore not safe to assume that things were the same. Given the social structures of the periods leading up to the Middle Ages, however, it would be feasible to suggest that marriages took place for political reasons, to secure inheritances with children, for domestic comfort, for lust and occasionally for love. Later evidence suggests that the general feeling among men was that, if one was to marry at all, prudence was essential regarding the choice of a mate. Writers for audiences of both men and women stressed that marriage was for children, and to secure the family inheritance, and that it was composed of honour, duty and chastity. Especially in Victorian times, the family was considered sacrosanct. Framed by love, duty, honour, and charity, it was the natural resting place away from the cares of the world. It represented unity and order and man depended on woman to provide him with such an environment, thus the selection of a mate was seen as being crucial to his future welfare.

What we cannot know is whether men debated the type of woman they wished to marry to the same extent as they appeared to during the Middle Ages and afterwards.

DISSERTATION ON THE BACHELOR

A lordly beast is the manéd lion,
And maketh a lordly prey;
While huntsmen thrill to be in at the kill
When the stag has turned at bay.
Crafty the fox inn the coverts brown,
And fierce the wolf at the door.
But the merriest game that roves the town
Is the frolicsome bachelor.

The bachelor, the bachelor,
His ways are the ways of guile.
But soon or late,
He takes the bait
And Lohengrins up the aisle.

By the light in his eye can you mark him out –
A confident, wary one;
While his gait divides between arrogant strides
And an air of ready-to-run.
Bold is the stripe in his striped cravat,
His trousers are creaséd well.
The furnished flat is his habitat,
Or the moderate-priced hotel.

The bachelor, the bachelor,
Though free as a questing seagull,
Some Frail-and-Fair
Will spot him there
To be her husband lee-gul.

By day he skulks in a bachelor world
That womenkind seldom swoop on.
He argues in courts or files reports
Or cheerfully clips a coupon;
Or seeks the place where the rainbow ends,
While he shuns the perilous blonde;
Or sells insurance to college friends,
Or studies the stock and bond.
But when the evening draweth nigh,
Emerges the bachelor clan –
From the bearless buck in his first white tie
To the battle-scarred veteran.
They saunter forth with the evening star,
To nibble the nut and the caviar,
To sip the Scotch and soda water,
And ogle their hostess's youngest daughter.
And some are handsome and some are horrid
And some are getting a hairless forehead,
And some bound lightly out of their thickets,
With fruit and flowers and theatre tickets;
And some run willingly off to dance,
And some creep softly, with sidewise glance,
And some stand stiffly, aloof, apart,
But each is marked for the marriage mart.
Though cunning or fleet as a desert pony,
He'll fall in the toils of matrimony.
He'll learn to fetch and he'll learn to carry
And have no peace till his comrades marry.

For the bachelor, the bachelor,
Though freedom is his proclivity,
He'll end a trophy
To Sally or Sophie,
And flourish in captivity.

Phyllis McGinley, *The Boudoir Companion*, 1938

Fiancés needed mother's approval as well as father's. *The Fiancés Visit* by Odulf Troost.

Dating from the fifteenth century, there exists a number of rhymes and poems which deal with the subject of women. One such, which begins

Man, bewar of thin wowyng,
For weddying is the longe wo

warns of widows who are only interested in spending a man's money, and young maidens who are 'fals and fekyl'. It is hard to find material in literature which defends marriage. There is a fair amount concerning the woes of marriage, the joys of bachelorhood and warnings to heed when selecting a wife. Of course, love prose and poetry exists from all periods, but it is rare to find the positive aspects of love and marriage highlighted together prior to the eighteenth century.

Advice, it seems, was plentiful. Much of it deals with choosing a wife, but there also exists material concerned with how to treat a wife. In 1837, William Cobbett wrote in his *Advice to a Lover:*

Marriage brings numerous cares, which are amply compensated by the more numerous delights which are their companions. But to have the delights, as well as the cares, the choice of the partner must be fortunate.

The kind of woman recommended by some seventeenth-century Catholics as being a suitable marriage companion had to conform to certain rules. Her eyes and ears saw and heard only what her husband thought appropriate and she spoke only when spoken to. Her heart, of course, was a place which she kept at peace, repressing her sexual self, cherishing her husband, and where her devotion to religion was nurtured.

He goes on to list the things his readers ought to desire in a wife.

1. Chastity; 2. Sobriety; 3. Industry; 4. Frugality; 5. Cleanliness; 6. Knowledge of domestic affairs; 7. Good temper; 8. Beauty. Chastity, perfect modesty, in word, deed, and even thought is so essential, that, without it, no female is fit to be a wife. It is not enough that a young woman abstain from everything approaching towards indecorum in her behaviour towards men; it is, with me, not enough that she cast down her eyes, or turn aside her head with a smile, when she hears an indelicate allusion: she ought to appear not to understand it, and to receive from it no more impression than if she were a post. A loose woman is a disagreeable acquaintance: what must she be then, as a wife?

Cobbett tackles almost every aspect of marriage. He warns against extravagant women and gives advice as to the most obvious signs of potential extravagant behaviour in young women. He even tackles household duties:

occasional cleanliness is not the thing that an English or an American husband wants: he wants it always: indoors as well as out; by night as well as by day; on the floor as well as on the table; . . .

'DO you care about dancing at all? I am not sure whether clever men ever dance.'

'I would dance with you, if you would allow me.'

'Oh!' said Rosamond, with a slight deprecatory laugh. 'I was only going to say that we sometimes have dancing, and I wanted to know whether you would feel insulted if you were asked to come.'

'Not on the condition I mentioned.'

After this chat Lydgate thought that he was going, but on moving towards the whist-tables, he got interested in watching Mr Farebrother's play, which was masterly, and also his face, which was a striking mixture of the shrewd and the mild. At ten o'clock supper was brought in (such were the customs of Middlemarch), and there was punch-drinking; but Mr Farebrother had only a glass of water. He was winning, but there seemed to be no reason why the renewal of rubbers should end, and Lydgate at last took his leave.

But as it was not eleven o'clock, he chose to walk in the brisk air towards the tower of St Botolph's, Mr Farebrother's church, which stood out dark, square, and massive against the starlight. It was the oldest church in Middlemarch; the living, however, was but a vicarage worth barely four hundred a-year. Lydgate had heard that, and he wondered now whether Mr Farebrother cared about the money he won at cards. . . .

These were actually Lydgate's first meditations as he walked away from Mr Vincy's, and on this ground I fear that many ladies will consider him hardly worthy of their attention. He thought of Rosamond and her music only in the second place; and though, when her turn came, he dwelt on the image of her for the rest of his walk, he felt no agitation, and had no sense that any new current had set into his life. He could not marry yet; he wished not to marry for several years; and therefore he was not ready to entertain the notion of being in love with a girl whom he happened to admire. He did admire Rosamond exceedingly; but that madness which had once beset him about Laure was not, he thought, likely to recur in relation to any other woman. Certainly, if falling in love had been at all in question, it would have been quite safe with a creature like this Miss Vincy, who had just the kind of intelligence one would desire in a woman – polished, refined, docile, lending itself to finish in all the delicacies of life, and enshrined in a body which expressed this with a force of demonstration that excluded the need for other evidence. Lydgate felt sure that if ever he married, his wife would have that feminine radiance, that distinctive womanhood which must be classed with flowers and music, that sort of beauty which by its very nature was virtuous, being moulded only for pure and delicate joys.

But since he did not mean to marry for the next five years – his more pressing business was to look into Louis' new book on Fever, which he was specially interested in, because he had known Louis in Paris, and had followed many anatomical demonstrations in order to ascertain the specific differences of typhus and typhoid. He went home and read far into the smallest hour, bringing a much more testing vision of details and relations into this pathological study than he had ever thought it necessary to apply to the complexities of love and marriage, these being subjects on which he felt himself amply informed by literature, and that traditional wisdom which is handed down in the genial conversation of men.

George Eliot, *Middlemarch*

DISAGREEABLE ACQUIESCENCE.

PARKER (*on the eve of his wedding-day*). "Gentlemen, I—I—I—er—"
BRONSON (*misogynist*). "Indeed you do, Parker. Any man who gives up bachelor joys for marriage cares errs dreadfully."

The male view of marriage from the 1894 edition of *Harper's Monthly*.

NOTWITHSTANDING your Happiness and your recommendation I hope I shall never marry. Though the most beautiful Creature were waiting for me at the end of a Journey or a Walk; though the Carpet were of Silk, the Curtains of the morning Clouds; the chairs and Sofa stuffed with Cygnet' down; the food Manna, the Wine beyond Claret, the Window opening on Winander mere, I should not feel – or rather my Happiness would not be so fine, as my Solitude is sublime. Then instead of what I have described, there is a sublimity to welcome me home – The roaring of the wind is my wife and the Stars through the window pane are my Children. The mighty abstract Idea I have of Beauty in all things stifles the more divided and minute domestic happiness – an amiable wife and sweet Children I contemplate as a part of that Beauty, but I must have a thousand of those beautiful particles to fill up my heart. I feel more and more every day, as my imagination strengthens, that I do not live in this world alone but in a thousand worlds – No sooner am I alone than shapes of epic greatness are stationed around me, and serve my Spirit the office which is equivalent to a King's bodyguard – then 'Tragedy with sceptred pall comes sweeping by'. According to my state of mind I am with Achilles shouting in the Trenches, or with Theocritus in the Vales of Sicily. Or I throw my whole being into Troilus, and repeating those lines, 'I wander like a lost Soul upon the stygian Banks staying for waftage,' I melt into the air with a voluptuousness so delicate that I am content to be alone. These things, combined with the opinion I have of the generality of women – who appear to me as children to whom I would rather give a sugar Plum than my time, form a barrier against Matrimony which I rejoice in.

John Keats, *Letter to George and Georgiana Keats*,
25 October 1818

Cobbett covers just about every question a man might have on the subject. He concludes that a man might tell a woman's 'mark of industry', by her quick step and a 'somewhat heavy tread showing that the foot comes down with a hearty good will . . .'

Once married, men bemoaned the problem of 'bad wives'. One solution, as we have seen, was to sell one's wife, but other men counselled on the situation, chiding young and inexperienced men who resorted to blows when dealing with their spouses. One writer in the sixteenth century recommended using both 'a carrot and a stick to bring about companionship'.

Christmas Day, 1665

TO church in the morning, and there saw a wedding in the church, which I have not seen many a day, and the young people so merry one with another; and so strange, to see what delight we married people have to see these poor fools decoyed into our condition, every man and wife gazing and smiling at them.

Samuel Pepys, *Diary*

A man would sometimes weigh up in his mind the advantages and disadvantages of getting married before he even contemplated the search. In 1859 the famous Pre-Raphaelite painter, William Holman Hunt, wrote to his friends the Combes in Oxford with a description of the kind of girl he would like to marry:

preferably 5 feet 6 or 7 with rather aquiline nose, long round neck and very beautiful – complexion either fair or dark if good and nor more than 24, you must first ascertain that she is not engaged and that she could be content to live on about £500 a year . . . Birth or money rather a disadvantage than otherwise.

Such men as farmers, for whom a wife would have been an economic necessity were, presumably, less exacting in their choice.

The History of Courtship

IT is possible for a spinster to be disappointed in lovers, but only the married are
ever disappointed in love.

Myrtle Reed, *The Spinster Book*, 1903

Until the social upheavals of the early twentieth century changed courtship
rituals and permitted the freedom to go out on dates, one might question
how a young man and a young woman got to know each other. The
answer, of course, is that many people, from all walks of life, were little more than
acquaintances on their wedding day. Men and women expected to marry, but the
matter of whom they might marry was often beyond their control; thus courtship had
little or no part in marital arrangements. The opportunity of getting to know one
another in the hopes of falling in love was quite unnecessary at a time when love was
a rare factor of marriage.

———————— ♡ ————————

COURTSHIP is a game that a girl has to
play without knowing the trump. The
only way she ever succeeds at it is by
playing to an imaginary trump of her own,
which may be open, disarming friendli-
ness, or simple indifference.

Myrtle Reed, *The Spinster Book*, 1903

———————— ♡ ————————

Courtship today – 'dating', or 'going out', as we would say today – plays a far
more important role in our lives than it did in the past. Yet courtship rituals have
existed in society for centuries. Many scholars have suggested that the roots of
contemporary courtship lie in the courtly love traditions of the twelfth century when
there emerged from the Provençal region of southern France a type of love which
idealized women. This became immensely popular, ultimately spreading throughout

A Courting Couple by Jules Arsène Garnier.

Europe. Curiously enough, the basis of this love form was that of a knight's love for a married lady, so courtship between two unattached people as we think of it today started out under a different guise.

A man and woman of the nobility (this is the only class in which the convention of courtly love existed), would not expect on their wedding day to be in love with each other, and although mutual affection, and even love, might develop over the years it was not anticipated by either party. Outside the marriage, however, love could flourish. Whilst a woman would find harsh punishment awaiting her should she commit adultery, a married man, although expected by society to honour his wife, nonetheless could take a mistress without his wife having recourse to retribution. Yet once married and mistress of her own home, with her husband away for months at a time, a woman enjoyed far greater freedom and closer intimacy in the daily company of the lord's knights as she ran the estate in conjunction with his stewards. The lord tolerated a relationship between knight and lady because it was the convention of the time. In fact, he paraded his lady in front of the knights, encouraging their adoration, so that when he left for battle he left behind him a tense situation between a knight and his wife.

Off-duty knights, without battles to occupy them, became troubadours entertaining the court with their songs of love and valour. When one thinks of troubadours today there comes to mind the image of a pale young man strumming a lute. In fact, many troubadours were first-born sons who were filling in time waiting for their fathers to die so that they might claim their inheritance. Others were the second sons of noble families, impoverished social outcasts who, under the rules of primogeniture, were unable to inherit. These men looked to make their livelihood from the booty of battle and on the jousting circuit. Many such a young man had slender hopes of marrying. Few fathers would look favourably upon the suit of a poor nobleman, so a great number remained bachelors throughout their lives, devoting themselves instead to one married woman and becoming her champion even if later they did eventually marry someone else. Well-groomed and perfumed, with no trace of the battlefield evident, the troubadour entertained his lady by writing songs to amuse her and sang her praises to the court at large.

Directed to an aristocratic audience made up largely of women, the songs were not only of love, but of war and political strife, and they focused on the romantic themes of Celtic tales and the Knights of the Round Table at the fifth-century court of King Arthur. Often, the lady of the song would remain anonymous, because if her husband should find offence in the verses, the singer would be banished from court. With the elaborate role-playing that can only thrive in an atmosphere where wealth under-writes leisure, and education offers inspiration and food for imagination, the troubadours' songs raised the noblewoman from chattel and child-bearer to a more goddess-like creature.

There were over five hundred troubadours and they travelled from one court to another in France, Italy, Sicily, Spain, Germany and England. As television today assists in popularizing romantic ideas, so the songs of the troubadours in the past

Chivalrous knights and their ladies fired the imaginations of nineteenth-century painters such as Sir Frank Dicksee: *La Belle Dame Sans Merci.*

reached a wide audience, and in a short time the concept of courtly love swept across Europe, fuelled by books on the subject of chivalry and the duties of knighthood.

A number of reasons have been suggested for the development of courtly love, as this form of love came to be called, during the Middle Ages. Certainly, the idea rooted and spread rapidly at a time when marital love was rare. In attempting to explain this idolization of women – which was at the centre of courtly love – at a point in history when their general status was low and they were viewed as sinners, some historians have been able to trace a cult of the Virgin Mary to the twelfth century. It is worth noting also the presence of Catalan minstrels in southern France who brought with them Arabic and Spanish love songs, a number of which dealt with the themes of unrequited love and the adoration of women. (Spanish women in general were treated much better than their English, French or Italian counterparts.) The tradition that the suitor was supposed to remain chaste for the woman of his affection might relate to the fact that the troubadour culture prospered in the Languedoc region of France where Catharism had emerged. The Cathars felt that Christ was the only good force in life, and that all else was evil – especially anything to do with the flesh; they had a horror of sex and cherished virginity. But perhaps most important of all was the

The stiffness of the figures did not reflect on the nature of courtship in the fifteenth century. This work is entitled *Love at First Sight* (Anon.).

fact that court life was extremely crowded, bringing the sexes together with many people under the same roof. A code of etiquette was necessary, therefore, in order to maintain social order.

Tracing courtship over the centuries we also encounter chivalry as being an important facet of the ritual. While the history of courtly love is closely related to that of chivalry, the latter originated in the warrior traditions of pagan Europe. From the Middle Ages chivalry became a code of conduct for knights all over Europe and it has been linked to feudalism, but whereas feudalism was a means of defining and structuring society, chivalry was concerned with the demeanour and ethical values of one class of society only, the nobility. The aristocracy was already linked to the military, as the army was the traditional repository for second sons unable to inherit under the rules of primogeniture, but the values of chivalry spread much further than the ranks of knights and came to be associated over the centuries not only with fighting but also with ritual and ceremony, and a code of conduct, the remnants of which can still be seen today.

When we think of the proverbial knight in shining armour we bring to mind the Victorian version of the hero of medieval legends. In reality, the kindly fellow on a white charger rescuing damsels in distress, as we think of the knight today, and the knight of the Middle Ages were probably two quite different people. Our view is tainted by the romanticism and dramatization of the knight and his role which occurred over the centuries, particularly during the nineteenth century. For the medieval knight was, appropriately for his times, both brutal and bloodthirsty; indeed, some scholars have suggested that the purpose of the chivalric code was to make the face of war more acceptable.

Six hundred years after the emergence of the chivalrous knight the remnants of the chivalric code and the courtly love convention could still be clearly seen in Victorian times: as a general code of behaviour for gentlemen as opposed to ordinary men; in the platonic love rituals of the upper classes who, like their medieval counterparts, had both the time and the education to appreciate the games involved; and as a code of practice for courtship.

If he wasn't one by birth, a man born in the eighteenth or nineteenth century might aspire to becoming a 'gentleman'. Certainly, he would be familiar with an unwritten code of ethics that described the behaviour of gentlemen. Boys in English public schools were educated to 'be men' by becoming good athletes, able to endure certain hardships, and they were encouraged to be honourable men, who took care of the poor and were faithful to their wives.

Courtship fourteenth-century style, with the bed featuring prominently, at the court of Burgundy in France.

The rules of courtship were often broken.

In the upper levels of society, the vestiges of the chivalric code were seen in the way in which a man paid court to another man's wife. This type of situation occurred when, for instance, the wife of an important minister whose work took him away from home a great deal required an escort. Many of these women became known as the great hostesses of their time, attracting admirers to their salons and country homes, and while in theory the relationships were platonic, the practice was often quite different.

The Victorians thought nothing of long engagements when love was supposed to survive on an irregular exchange of letters, of chaperoned visits, of ardent declarations of love from men (within the confines of an established relationship), of the elaborate forms of address that a man used when courting a woman, or of a man bending on one knee offering to be the 'servant' of the woman he wished to marry – even though, of course, on the surface medieval courtly love had nothing to do with marriage. Of course, once the man and woman were married things were often very different. The husband would shelter and protect his wife in a proper chivalrous manner, attempting to keep her 'pure', but no longer did the offer stand to be her servant.

The real roots of modern-day courtship lie in both the courtly love convention and the chivalric code as well as the rituals of the poorer classes. It is important to state here that courtship for the rich and courtship for the poor were quite different, only beginning to merge in the nineteenth century with the middle classes. For the wealthy daughter or son, courtship was conducted at a distance, supervised and largely controlled by parents – although elopements testify to a lack of vigil in chaperones and strong desire on the part of the young couple concerned to dispense with

controlled by parents – although elopements testify to a lack of vigil in chaperones and strong desire on the part of the young couple concerned to dispense with convention. The daughters of the middle and upper classes were only able to meet men chosen by their parents. In literature we read about 'gentlemen callers', bringing wanted and unwanted attentions, seeking permission from father to 'pay court' to his daughter. However, the arranged marriage society did not exist for the very poor, who had nothing to give or gain from it. We have already seen how a poor woman enjoyed greater freedom in many respects, including the ability to marry a man of her choice rather than someone imposed on her by her father. In a society where people were free to marry whomsoever they chose, we imagine that they would take time to select a partner and review a number of options before doing so.

The study of the history of courtship reveals a strange custom called 'bundling' – whose origins have proved hard to trace. Bundling was the practice of putting a young couple together in one room for the night. The girl would be heavily clothed, particularly on the lower half of her body, and often her ankles, calves or thighs were tied together. She would sleep in a bed alongside a bolster or wooden board, across from which would be a young man. Despite all the barricades, some young women became pregnant. The practice of bundling thrived in England and the northern states of America for several centuries prior to this one, existing almost exclusively in rural communities. It has been suggested that the need for warmth encouraged people to huddle together, although more realistic interpretations would lead one to assume that this was a form of dating, an acceptance on behalf of the parents that the couple should get to know and like each other but in circumstances under parental control.

It would be impossible to chart the actual course of courtship over the centuries. All

The curious custom of bundling allowed a young couple to spend the night together before they were married.

young men and women came into contact with each other while looking for work and during their working days, especially if they were servants. Meetings, which were initially held in groups, lead to the young man visiting the girl at her parents' house, where he would be permitted to sit and talk to her in the company of her family. Like girls of all classes the poor girl was initially supposed to demur and not give any encouragement to her prospective suitor; politeness was all that was required of her. If she found nothing objectionable in the young man she would, like her wealthy counterpart, expect to give him enough encouragement to visit her again without appearing to be forward or too eager. If enquiries into the suitor's background and means of living proved favourable, then negotiations could begin for the betrothal and nuptials.

There was, of course, etiquette to observe, but it is impossible to say if this changed from century to century. In the nineteenth century, and certainly before, a man did not walk arm-in-arm with a girl unless he intended to marry her, and even then such familiarity would attract disapproval.

The popularization of dating as we would recognize it today is directly related to the demise of the arranged marriage in all levels of society. Without pressure to marry someone, or even to marry at all, men and women are free to get to know each other in a fashion that would have been unthinkable less than one hundred years ago.

A suitor had to contend with many obstacles. *The New Suitor* by Eugene von de Blaas.

Will You Marry Me?

Marry'd in haste, we may repent at leisure.

William Congreve, *The Old Bachelor*

*D*id men in the past get down on bended knee to propose any more than they do now? It is doubtful. There were more written proposals of marriage, since communication by letter – before the arrival of the telephone – was commonplace anyway, and the correct way for a man to address a woman, especially if he had some doubts as to whether his affections were likely to be returned. Given that many marriages prior to the nineteenth century were arranged between the parents of the bride and groom, or the groom and the bride's parents, it is unlikely that the kind of lengthy, romantic proposal we envision actually existed at all. There must have been some proposal – manners and morals would have determined that the man at least ask the woman, even if her answer was already known to him – but the agonizing wait for an answer, which we associate with eighteenth- and nineteenth-century novels, must have come later, hand in hand with a greater freedom amongst the parties to choose their partners.

———————— ○ ————————

NOTHING strengthens a woman's self-confidence like a proposal. One is a wonder, two a superfluity, and three an epidemic. Four are proof of unusual charm, five go to the head, and it is a rare girl whom six or seven will not permanently spoil.

Myrtle Reed, *The Spinster Book*, 1903

———————— ○ ————————

26 May, 1820
The Earl of Erroll to Miss Gascoyne
6 Duke St. St. James's

MY dear Miss Gascoyne,

I have received a letter from General Sir Hussey Vivian, in which he requests me to acquaint him immediately whether it is my intention or not to proceed to Ireland to join Sir Colquhon Grant as it is absolutely necessary for me to decide.

Previous to making this decision I most anxiously wish to see you particularly after what passed between us on that subject the other evening.

May I entreat you to send me word as to what hour I may call tomorrow?

I would have left this myself but am confined to the house with a wretched cold which prevents me from personally enquiring after Mrs Gascoyne and yourself.

I remain, my dear Miss Gascoyne, yours most sincerely,

ERROLL

Carola Oman, *The Gascoyne Heiress*

THE PROPOSAL

THE number of men today who ask, in so many words, that a girl marry them is probably very limited, despite the testimony of the movies and fiction. The engagement is usually approached by a very circuitous route, probably because young people now have ample opportunity to spend time in each other's company and to know each other well before any discussion of marriage takes place. Victorian times must have been very difficult for suitors, because it was only after they had proposed, and received father's consent, that they had any opportunity to know the girl of their choice. And even then contact was on the most restricted plane and sternly chaperoned.

Any girl with common sense knows when a man is trying to propose and either helps him commit himself or discourages him from doing so before he has gone too far. It is certainly unkind to encourage the expression of a proposal only to turn it down. Yet an obstinate coyness on the part of the girl who would really like to accept a proposal, were it offered, often deters a man, who fears he will be refused. In other words, it is up to the woman, at the right time, to let a man know that a proposal, if offered, will be accepted.

Amy Vanderbilt's Complete Book of Etiquette, 1952

Francis Mary Gascoyne-Cecil received her first proposal of marriage at the age of seventeen from George Canning, Baron Garvagh, who was forty-one years old.

I deem it to be the most manly and the most honourable mode, for one who feels as I do, to make a frank and full avowal of his sentiments, for which, though I entreat your indulgence, I cannot confess myself to be ashamed. And when I declare to you, as I hereby do, that I entertain the strongest attachment and love for you, I am confident that this confession is made to One possessed of qualities which, whatever Her decision, will not suffer Her to treat otherwise than with tenderness, the most anxious and the most dear communications which a Man can make to a Woman. Having thus undisguisedly stated to you my feelings, I entreat and I implore of you to make me happy by consenting to become united with me, and I do so with the ardour and with the humility to which you are eminently entitled, and with which every Man of spirit must feel himself impressed when he solicits the Lady whom he loves.

For myself, I have nothing to plead except my sincere devotion to you, for I seek nor desire no other boon than but yourself and with you I should be supremely happy. And should you bless me with a favourable reception, the study of my life should be to make you happy by every constant attention and kindness that the fondest affection can inspire. As I perceive that the first avowal of attachment is due, in the first instance to Her who has inspired it, I addressed this letter to you without any previous communication with your Parents, but that I might not, by thus approaching you, appear guilty of indelicacy towards a Young Lady, for whom I feel every tenderness and every respect, I have enclosed it unsealed to your Father. Should you deem its contents or its author worthy of your consideration my next happiness would be to be permitted by you to address each of your Parents and to implore their consent whom it would ever be my delight as well as my duty, constantly to cultivate and to respect.

With repeated sentiments of attachment and of affection I conclude this letter, by again imploring your consent and favour and I subscribe myself as I feel

Your most sincere and devoted
GARVAGH

Hertford St. 25 June, 1819.

Proposals have nearly always been entirely private matters. *The Proposal* by Otto Erdman.

Many proposals were couched in such terms that should the letter fall into the hands of a girl's parent it would not read as inappropriate or impertinent. Many men addressed the girl's father, asking permission for his daughter's hand in marriage before they approached the girl themselves and, once receiving permission to speak to the daughter, felt that with the father's approval the answer must surely be 'yes'. Others preferred to speak directly to the girl and, having obtained her agreement, then approached her father.

A proposal is still one of the most private things between a couple, wherever it takes place – in a hay stack, the living room of a parent's home or in a restaurant. Some written proposals have survived to give us an indication as to the way in which a woman was addressed on this subject. Few rejections have survived; one assumes that these were not retained as keepsakes amongst family papers.

WILL YOU MARRY ME?

'LOOK here, Anne,' he presently said. 'How soon can we be married?'

Anne faltered. Her heart throbbed.

'How soon?' she asked. 'As soon as that?'

'I want us to be married.'

Anne felt her colour rising. She had not thought of marriage. When she spoke, her voice was unsteady.

'I wasn't prepared for that,' she murmured. 'I thought we should go on – being engaged – for . . . oh, for perhaps a year.'

'I couldn't wait,' said Mortimer. He was urgent. The grip of his elbow, which pressed Anne's hand to his side, was greater. His shoulder was against her breast. Anne, glancing up, met eyes that burned. In her heart she was flurried, although her encounter with Mortimer's urgent gaze was straight.

'Oh!' laughed Anne. But she was much moved. 'I shall have to think about it.'

'No, no. If you think, you'll delay. Why shouldn't we marry? Why wait till the sweets are familiar?'

'Will they ever be that?' Anne was shy, wondering. 'I didn't suppose they staled very quickly.'

'I want you,' said Mortimer, imperiously.

'And you mustn't be kept waiting?' she questioned. But she was arch to no purpose. The impulse, indeed, had been confused. The clear face of Mortimer was close to her own. She saw his eager lips, his eyes demanding; and the archness, at first so half-hearted, died wholly. Was not this surrender to her lover's will what she most desired? It was a mystery to herself – a mystery unread, veiled, a perplexity. Whatever her desire had been, this, at least, was true, that she had no immediate answer to Mortimer's importunity. Anne sighed; but the sigh was not an unhappy one. She continued: 'Mortimer, you really *must* let me think!'

'Is there any reason?' He was unanswerable.

'None . . . except . . .' Anne hesitated. 'Except that I haven't thought about it'

'Do you think about everything? Until there's no impulse left?'

There was something ugly in his tone, as though he sneered at her character; and Anne flinched from his attack. It was both unexpected and bitter. Did he love her?

'Do I deserve that?' she parried, fighting unarmed.

'I'm asking you.' Mortimer chose to be exigent. Anne felt her heart plunge at his tone. She started, and stared. The first word that rose to her lips was checked; but there was the smallest drop of horror amid her warm love for him.

'Suppose we say it's my impulse to hesitate?' asked Anne, at last. 'As it certainly is. Mortimer, I don't like being rushed. I don't like to talk as you're doing. I don't see any good in it. Remember, you've been *thinking* about this. You've got it all clear. It's new to me.' She paused an instant before concluding. 'Do be patient with me.'

There was resoluteness in Anne's tone which she was far from finding in her heart. There, she felt, all was weakness. And, to increase this doubt, Mortimer shrugged. His face was set. She had never before seen him so uncontrollable. In vain did Anne search for any softening of his expression. There was a long silence. Then, at last, as they continued upon their way, Anne was seized with an idea.

'Mortimer,' she said, suddenly. 'I . . . I hate to say it; but a wife – a wife is an expense. . . . Have you thought of that?'

'O-oh!' It was clear that he found her too matter-of-fact. Anne felt her cheeks growing hot. Then the tension was strangely relaxed. 'Not a great expense,' said Mortimer, as he still frowningly looked askance. The pressure of his arm dimished. 'Besides—' He stopped abruptly. Then, as she waited, he resumed: 'Besides, need you . . . at first . . . give up your own work. I thought you could—'

'Oh, Mortimer!' It was out – a cry of disappointment. Anne's heart felt cold. She, too, allowed her clasp, which had been so happy, slightly to loosen. Quickly, she tried to recover whatever might have been lost to them both by that exclamation. 'I'm sorry,' she said. 'I could very likely keep on at Kilburn's. I'm almost sure I could. Wouldn't it be better to wait? I think you're greedy for us both. Don't let's decide now.'

'I can't wait,' Mortimer persisted, clouded and obstinate. He stared straight ahead of him; his mouth seemed to tremble, and the muscles of his throat. 'If you love me, you'll see what a life I lead—'

'*If* I love you!' breathed Anne. Mortimer took no notice of her protest.

'I can't bear this loneliness any longer. I want you, because if you don't come now I shall go mad. You've no idea—' He was speaking impetuously, his voice strained and earnest, as if he were in an extremity of emotion. 'You've simply no idea what it is to work all day and go home in the evening to a lodging where there's no home, no love, no interest; to have to kill time; to try to read and think – and fail; to come out in desperation into the streets, and see nobody one loves—'

'But, dearest,' cried Anne, almost weeping. 'I *do* love you. I do indeed.'

'You refuse what I ask.'

'I don't. But think! If I were to keep on working at an office I couldn't easily keep house for you. I should have to hurry off in the morning, and come home to my housework after you had been home some time. You'd get home to an untidy house – with no comfort, no wife to greet you . . . And I—'

'Only for a time. Only until I could earn enough money for us both. If I had you, I could earn more. It would encourage me.'

'But you could come every evening to see us at home. We could be together.'

'Not really together. Never the door closed, and us two alone in the world. Oh, no, no, Anne; I'm right in this. My dear, don't let us waste any time. Let's get married *now*, and settle the details later.'

Anne shook her head. She was troubled.

'It's spoiling it!' she cried, sharply.

'Spoiling it!' Mortimer's exclamation was equally sharp. 'I don't know what you mean.'

'I mean that we should begin wrong.'

'I don't agree.'

They walked onward now, both of them dismayed by their talk and by the difference which lay between them. Every time Anne thought of the proposed arrangement she shook her head. It was unwise. That was all she could say. It was unwise. Her heart was in conflict with her good sense. Her heart told her that

Mortimer needed her, and that nothing must stand before the assuagement of his need. Her experience showed her that such a marriage began in passion and ended in estrangement. All her hopes had been for a little home of which she could be the mistress and Mortimer the master of it all.

Evening fell quickly now; the shadows crept upon them, at first lingeringly, and then with a swooping of darkness. Already Anne could scarcely see Mortimer's face. She still kept her hand tucked within the crook of his arm, but that arm was no longer warm and possessive, but stiff with a mood of aversion. Anne felt her lips pucker into a smile; and indeed she thought Mortimer was being unreasonable. But she neither smiled nor spoke. She walked soberly enough by his side, wondering. After all, a young man was no easy problem for a young woman to solve. Mortimer, especially, was a very difficult one for Anne. Anne loved him.

'Aren't you being rather cruel?' she presently asked him, in a low voice.

Frank Swinnerton, *The Elder Sister*

AND they walked on so in silence, while the warm tears fell. Adam was content, and said nothing. It was Dinah who spoke first.

'Adam,' she said, 'it is the Divine Will. My soul is so knit to yours that it is but a divided life I live without you. And this moment, now you are with me, and I feel that our hearts are filled with the same love, I have a fulness of strength to bear and do our heavenly Father's Will, that I had lost before.'

Adam paused and looked into her sincere eyes.

'Then we'll never part any more, Dinah, till death parts us.'

And they kissed each other with a deep joy.

What greater thing is there for two human souls, than to feel that they are joined for life – to strengthen each other in all labour, to rest on each other in all sorrow, to minister to each other in all pain, to be one with each other in silent unspeakable memories at the moment of the last parting?

George Eliot, *Adam Bede*

Rejected Addresses (Anon.).

HOW and when a man proposes is a problem of heart and impulse rather than etiquette. It is safe to say that the proposal is rarely unexpected, and that the young woman is prepared for the man's declaration of love.

The sensible young woman of today does not rush blindly into marriage. The most serious mistake a young girl can make is to promise herself in marriage to a young man she thinks she loves but with whose tastes and ideals she is absolutely out of harmony. If the proposal leaves her struggling with her ideals and her impulses, she should avoid a definite answer and put it off until she can be sure of herself. A moment's weakness can cause a lifetime of pain, and the answer to a proposal should be given only after clear, calm thought and deliberation.

It is no longer customary to 'ask father', though the cartoonists and humorists would have us believe so. There are few traces of stilted artificiality remaining in our betrothal customs; the formal proposal on bended knee and the formal consent of the young lady's father are things of the past. However, as soon as a young man and woman have definitely decided to marry, they go, if they are at all well-bred and considerate, to the young lady's parents and ask their approval. Unless it has been romantic 'love at first sight' with courtship and betrothal all in a week, the parents will probably have heard of the young man and know something about him. At this time, when the young man imparts the happy news that he has been accepted by their daughter, it is the parents' privilege to ask him whatever questions they deem advisable concerning his business and his ability to provide for their daughter. To all questions he must reply with candor and politeness.

If the parents disapprove of the betrothal, the young woman must decide for herself whether she wishes to sacrifice her own happiness to that of her mother and father. The modern girl marries the man of her choice and is usually sensible enough to know when the choice is right. Therefore, unless the parents have a very real reason for objecting to the young man, they should not be so selfish as to stand in the way of their daughter's happiness. If they find something to disapprove of in the young man, they should discuss it with him frankly, and he will probably make every effort to correct his fault or prove his stability.

Lillian Eichler, *The New Book of Etiquette*, 1936

'I grieve to leave Thornfield: I love Thornfield: – I love it, because I have lived in it a full and delightful life – momentarily at least. I have not been trampled on. I have not been petrified. I have not been buried with inferior minds, and excluded from every glimpse of communion with what is bright and energetic, and high. I have talked, face to face, with what I reverence; with what I delight in, – with an original, a vigorous, an expanded mind. I have known you, Mr Rochester; and it strikes me with terror and anguish to feel I absolutely must be torn from you for ever. I see the necessity of departure; and it is like looking on the necessity of death.'

'Where do you see the necessity?' he asked, suddenly.

'Where? You, sir, have placed it before me.'

'In what shape?'

'In the shape of Miss Ingram; a noble and beautiful woman, – your bride.'

'My bride! What bride? I have no bride!'

'But you will have.'

'Yes: – I will! – I will!' He set his teeth.

'Then I must go: – you have said it yourself.'

'No: you must stay! I swear it – and the oath shall be kept.'

'I tell you I must go!' I retorted, roused to something like passion. 'Do you think I can stay to become nothing to you? Do you think I am an automaton? – a machine without feelings? and can bear to have my morsel of bread snatched from my lips, and my drop of living water dashed from my cup? Do you think, because I am poor, obscure, plain, and little, I am soulless and heartless? You think wrong! – I have as much soul as you, – and full as much

heart! And if God had gifted me with some beauty, and much wealth, I should have made it as hard for you to leave me, as it is now for me to leave you. I am not talking to you now through the medium of custom, conventionalities, or even of mortal flesh: – it is my spirit that addresses your spirit; just as if both had passed through the grave, and we stood at God's feet, equal, – as we are!'

'As we are!' repeated Mr Rochester – 'so,' he added, enclosing me in his arms, gathering me to his breast, pressing his lips on my lips: 'so, Jane!'

'Yes, so, sir,' I rejoined: 'and yet not so; for you are a married man – or as good as a married man, and wed to one inferior to you – to one with whom you have no sympathy – whom I do not believe you truly love; for I have seen and heard you sneer at her. I would scorn such a union: therefore I am better than you – let me go!'

'Where, Jane? To Ireland?'

'Yes – to Ireland. I have spoken my mind, and can go anywhere now.'

'Jane, be still; don't struggle so, like a wild, frantic bird that is rending its own plumage in its desperation.'

'I am no bird; and no net ensnares me; I am a free human being with an independent will; which I now exert to leave you.'

Another effort set me at liberty, and I stood erect before him.

'And your will shall decide your destiny,' he said: 'I offer you my hand, my heart, and a share of all my possessions.'

'You play a farce, which I merely laugh at.'

'I ask you to pass through life at my side – to be my second self and best earthly companion.'

'For that fate you have already made your choice, and must abide by it.'

'Jane, be still a few moments: you are over-excited: I will be still too.'

A waft of wind came sweeping down the laurel-walk, and trembled through the boughs of the chestnut: it wandered away – away – to an indefinite distance – it died. The nightingale's song was then the only voice of the hour: in listening to it, I again wept. Mr Rochester sat quiet, looking at me gently and seriously. Some time passed before he spoke: he at last said:

'Come to my side, Jane, and let us explain and understand one another.'

'I will never again come to your side: I am torn away now, and cannot return.'

'But, Jane, I summon you as my wife: it is you only I intend to marry.'

I was silent: I thought he mocked me.

'Come, Jane – come hither.'

'Your bride stands between us.'

He rose, and with a stride reached me.

'My bride is here,' he said, again drawing me to him, 'because my equal is here, and my likeness. Jane, will you marry me?'

Still I did not answer, and still I writhed myself from his grasp: for I was still incredulous.

'Do you doubt me, Jane?'

'Entirely.'

'You have no faith in me?'

'Not a whit.'

'Am I a liar in your eyes?' he asked passionately. 'Little sceptic, you *shall* be convinced. What love have I for Miss Ingram? None: and that you know. What love has she for me? None: as I have taken pains to prove: I caused a rumour to reach her that my fortune was not a third of what was supposed, and after that I pre-

sented myself to see the result; it was coldness both from her and her mother. I would not – I could not – marry Miss Ingram. You – you strange – you almost unearthly thing! – I love as my own flesh. You – poor and obscure, and small and plain as you are – I entreat to accept me as a husband.'

'What, me!' I ejaculated: beginning in his earnestness – and especially in his incivility – to credit his sincerity: 'me who have not a friend in the world but you – if you are my friend: not a shilling but what you have given me?'

'You, Jane. I must have you for my own – entirely my own. Will you be mine? Say yes, quickly.'

'Mr Rochester, let me look at your face: turn to the moonlight.'

'Why?'

'Because I want to read your countenance; turn!'

'There: you will find it scarcely more legible than a crumpled, scratched page. Read on: only make haste, for I suffer.'

His face was very much agitated and very much flushed, and there were strong workings in the features, and strange gleams in the eyes.

'Oh, Jane, you torture me!' he exclaimed. 'With that searching and yet faithful and generous look, you torture me!'

'How can I do that? If you are true and your offer real, my only feelings to you must be gratitude and devotion – they cannot torture.'

'Gratitude!' he ejaculated: and added wildly – 'Jane, accept me quickly. Say Edward – give me my name – Edward – I will marry you.'

'Are you in earnest? – Do you truly

love me? – Do you sincerely wish me to be your wife?'

'I do; and if an oath is necessary to satisfy you, I swear it.'

'Then, sir, I will marry you.'

'Edward – my little wife!'

'Dear Edward!'

'Come to me – come to me entirely now,' said he: and added, in his deepest tone, speaking in my ear as his cheek was laid on mine, 'Make my happiness – I will make yours.'

'God pardon me!' he subjoined ere long, 'and man meddle not with me: I have her, and will hold her.'

'There is no one to meddle, sir. I have no kindred to interfere.'

'No – that is the best of it,' he said. And if I had loved him less I should have thought his accent and look of exultation savage: but sitting by him, roused from the nightmare of parting – called to the paradise of union – I thought only of the bliss given me to drink in so abundant a flow. Again and again he said, 'Are you happy, Jane?' And again and again I answered, 'Yes.' After which he mur-

mured, 'It will atone – it will atone. Have I not found her friendless, and cold, and comfortless? Will I not guard, and cherish, and solace her? Is there not love in my heart, and constancy in my resolves? It will expiate at God's tribunal. I know my Maker sanctions what I do. For the world's judgment – I wash my hands thereof. For man's opinion – I defy it.'

But what had befallen the night? The moon was not yet set, and we were all in shadow: I could scarcely see my master's face, near as I was. And what ailed the chestnut tree? it writhed and groaned; while wind roared in the laurel walk, and came sweeping over us.

'We must go in,' said Mr Rochester: 'the weather changes. I could have sat with thee till morning, Jane.'

'And so,' thought I, 'could I with you.' I should have said so, perhaps, but a livid, vivid spark leapt out of a cloud at which I was looking, and there was a crack, a crash, and a close rattling peal; and I thought only of hiding my dazzled eyes against Mr Rochester's shoulder.

Charlotte Bronte, *Jane Eyre*

SHE rowed as well as she did many other things; and, though she used both hands, and Laurie but one, the oars kept time, and the boat went smoothly through the water.

'How well we pull together, don't we?' said Amy, who objected to silence just then.

'So well that I wish we might always pull in the same boat. Will you, Amy?' very tenderly.

'Yes, Laurie,' very low.

Then they both stopped rowing, and unconsciously added a pretty little tableau of human love and happiness to the dissolving views reflected in the lake.

Louisa M. Alcott, *Good Wives*

Such is the attitude of the man in William Powell Frith's *The Proposal* that one feels
the woman should say 'no'.

IT is very hard to tell whether a man
really means a proposal. It may have been
made under romantic circumstances, or
because he was lonesome for the other
girl, or, in the case of an heiress, because
he was tired of work.

Myrtle Reed, *The Spinster Book*, 1903

THE next day opened a new scene at Longbourn. Mr Collins made his declaration in form. Having resolved to do it without loss of time, as his leave of absence extended only to the following Saturday, and having no feelings of diffidence to make it distressing to himself even at the moment, he set about it in a very orderly manner, with all the observances, which he supposed a regular part of the business. On finding Mrs Bennet, Elizabeth, and one of the younger girls together, soon after breakfast, he addressed the mother in these words: 'May I hope, madam, for your interest with your fair daughter Elizabeth, when I solicit for the honour of a private audience with her in the course of this morning?'

Before Elizabeth had time for anything but a blush of suprise, Mrs Bennet instantly answered, 'Oh Dear ! – Yes – certainly. I am sure Lizzy will be very happy – I am sure she can have no objection. Come, Kitty, I want you upstairs.' And, gathering her work together, she was hastening away, when Elizabeth called out,

'Dear madam, do not go. I beg you will not go. Mr Collins must excuse me. He can have nothing to say to me that anybody need not hear. I am going away myself.'

'No, no, nonsense, Lizzy. I desire you will stay where you are.' And upon Elizabeth's seeming really, with vexed and embarrassed looks, about to escape, she added, 'Lizzy, I *insist* upon your staying and hearing Mr Collins.'

Elizabeth would not oppose such an injunction – and a moment's consideration making her also sensible that it would be wisest to get it over as soon and as quietly as possible, she sat down again, and tried to conceal, by incessant employment, the feelings which were divided between distress and diversion. Mrs Bennet and Kitty walked off, and as soon as they were gone Mr Collins began.

'Believe me, my dear Miss Elizabeth, that your modesty, so far from doing you any disservice, rather adds to your other perfections. You would have been less amiable in my eyes had there *not* been this little unwillingness; but allow me to assure you, that I have your respected mother's permission for this address. You can hardly doubt the purport of my discourse, however your natural delicacy may lead you to dissemble; my attentions have been too marked to be mistaken. Almost as soon as I entered the house, I singled you out as the companion of my future life. But before I am run away with by my feelings on this subject, perhaps it would be advisable for me to state my reasons for marrying – and, moreover, for coming into Hertfordshire with the design of selecting a wife, as I certainly did.'

The idea of Mr Collins, with all his solemn composure, being run away with by his feelings, made Elizabeth so near laughing, that she could not use the short pause he allowed in any attempt to stop him farther, and he continued: –

'My reasons for marrying are, first, that I think it a right thing for every clergyman in easy circumstances (like myself) to set the example of matrimony in his parish; secondly, that I am convinced it will add very greatly to my happiness; and thirdly – which perhaps I ought to have mentioned earlier, that it is the particular advice and recommendation of the very noble lady whom I have the honour of calling patroness. Twice has she condescended to give me her opinion (unasked too!) on this subject; and it was but the very Saturday night before I left Hunsford – between our pools at quadrille, while Mrs Jenkinson was arranging Miss de Bourgh's footstool, that she said, "Mr Collins, you must marry. A clergyman like you must marry. – Chuse properly, chuse a gentlewoman for *my* sake; and for your *own*, let her be an active, useful sort of person, not brought up high, but able to make a small income go a good way. This is my advice. Find such a woman as soon as you can, bring her to Hunsford, and I will visit her." Allow me, by the way, to observe, my fair cousin, that I do not reckon the notice and kindness of Lady Catherine de Bourgh as among the least of the advantages in my power to offer. You will find her manners beyond anything I can describe; and your wit and vivacity, I think, must be acceptable to her, especially when tempered with the silence and respect which her rank will inevitably excite. Thus much for my general intention in favour of matrimony; it remains to be told why my views were directed to Longbourn instead of my own neighbourhood, where I assure you there are many amiable young women. But the fact is, that being, as I am, to inherit this estate after the death of your honoured father (who, however, may live many years longer), I could not satisfy myself without resolving to chuse a wife from among his daughters, that the loss to them might be as little as possible, when the melancholy event takes place – which, however, as I have already said, may not be for several years. This has been my motive, my fair cousin, and I flatter myself it will not sink me in your esteem. And now nothing remains for me but to assure you in the most animated language of the violence of my affection.

To fortune I am perfectly indifferent, and shall make no demand of that nature on your father, since I am well aware that it could not be complied with; and that one thousand pounds in the 4 per cents., which will not be yours till after your mother's decease, is all that you may ever be entitled to. On that head, therefore, I shall be uniformly silent; and you may assure yourself that no ungenerous reproach shall ever pass my lips when we are married.'

It was absolutely necessary to interrupt him now.

'You are too hasty, sir,' she cried. 'You forget that I have made no answer. Let me do it without further loss of time. Accept my thanks for the compliment you are paying me. I am very sensible of the honour of your proposals, but it is impossible for me to do otherwise than decline them.'

'I am not now to learn,' replied Mr Collins, with a formal wave of the hand, 'that it is usual with young ladies to reject the addresses of the man whom they secretly mean to accept, when he first applies for their favour; and that sometimes the refusal is repeated a second or even a third time. I am therefore by no means discouraged by what you have just said, and shall hope to lead you to the altar ere long.'

'Upon my word, sir,' cried Elizabeth, 'your hope is rather an extraordinary one after my declaration. I do assure you that I am not one of those young ladies (if such young ladies there are) who are so daring as to risk their happiness on the chance of being asked a second time. I am perfectly serious in my refusal.

Jane Austen, *Pride and Prejudice*

BATHSHEBA'S aunt was indoors. 'Will you tell Miss Everdene that somebody would be glad to speak to her?' said Mr Oak. (Calling one's self merely Somebody, without giving a name, is not to be taken as an example of the ill-breeding of the rural world: it springs from a refined modesty of which townspeople, with their cards and announcements, have no notion whatever.)

Bathsheba was out. The voice had evidently been hers.

'Will you come in, Mr Oak?'

'Oh, thank 'ee,' said Gabriel, following her to the fireplace. 'I've brought a lamb for Miss Everdene. I thought she might like one to rear; girls do.'

'She might,' said Mrs Hurst musingly; 'though she's only a visitor here. If you will wait a minute Bathsheba will be in.'

'Yes, I will wait,' said Gabriel, sitting down. 'The lamb isn't really the business I came about, Mrs Hurst. In short, I was going to ask her if she'd like to be married.'

'And were you indeed?'

'Yes. Because if she would I should be very glad to marry her. D'ye know if she's got any other young man hanging about her at all?'

'Let me think,' said Mrs Hurst, poking the fire superfluously. . . . 'Yes – bless you, ever so many young men. You see, Farmer Oak, she's so good-looking, and an excellent scholar besides – she was going to be a governess once, you know, only she was too wild. Not that her young men ever come here – but, Lord, in the nature of women, she must have a dozen!'

'That's unfortunate,' said Farmer Oak, contemplating a crack in the stone floor with sorrow. 'I'm only an everyday sort of man, and my only chance was in being the first comer. . . . Well, there's no use in my waiting, for that was all I came about: so I'll take myself off home-along, Mrs Hurst.'

When Gabriel had gone about two hundred yards along the down, he heard a 'hoi-hoi!' uttered behind him, in a piping note of more treble quality than that in which the exclamation usually embodies itself when shouted across a field. He looked round, and saw a girl racing after him, waving a white handkerchief.

Oak stood still – and the runner drew nearer. It was Bathsheba Everdene. Gabriel's colour deepened: hers was already deep, not, as it appeared, from emotion, but from running.

'Farmer Oak – I—' she said, pausing for want of breath, pulling up in front of him with a slanted face, and putting her hand to her side.

'I have just called to see you,' said Gabriel pending her further speech.

'Yes – I know that,' she said, panting like a robin, her face red and moist from her exertions, like a peony petal before the sun dries off the dew. 'I didn't know you had come to ask to have me, or I should have come in from the garden instantly. I ran after you to say – that my aunt made a mistake in sending you away from courting me.'

Gabriel expanded. 'I'm sorry to have made you run so fast, my dear,' he said, with a grateful sense of favours to come. 'Wait a bit till you've found your breath.'

'– It was quite a mistake – aunt's telling you I had a young man already,' Bathsheba went on. 'I haven't a sweetheart at all – and I never had one, and I thought that, as times go with women, it was *such* a pity to send you away thinking that I had several.'

'Really and truly I am glad to hear that!' said Farmer Oak, smiling one of his long special smiles, and blushing with gladness. He held out his hand to take hers, which, when she had eased her side by pressing it there, was prettily extended upon her bosom to still her loud-beating heart. Directly he seized it she put it behind her, so that it slipped through his fingers like an eel.

'I have a nice snug little farm,' said Gabriel, with half a degree less assurance than when he had seized her hand.

'Yes; you have.'

'A man has advanced me money to begin with, but still, it will soon be paid off, and though I am only an every-day sort of man I have got on a little since I was a boy.' Gabriel uttered 'a little' in a tone to show her that it was the complacent form of 'a great deal.' He continued: 'When we be married, I am quite sure I can work twice as hard as I do now.'

He went forward and stretched out his arm again. Bathsheba had overtaken him at a point beside which stood a low stunted holly bush, now laden with red berries. Seeing his advance take the form of an attitude threatening a possible enclosure, if not compression, of her person, she edged off round the bush.

'Why, Farmer Oak,' she said over the top, looking at him with rounded eyes, 'I never said I was going to marry you.'

'Well – that *is* a tale!' said Oak with dismay. 'To run after anybody like this, and then say you don't want him!'

'What I meant to tell you was only this,' she said eagerly, and yet half conscious of the absurdity of the position she had made for herself – 'that nobody has got me yet as a sweetheart, instead of my having a dozen, as my aunt said; I *hate* to be thought men's property in that way, though possibly I shall be had some day. Why, if I'd wanted you I shouldn't have run after you like this; 'twould have been the *forwardest* thing! But there was no harm in hurrying to correct a piece of false news that had been told you.'

'Oh, no – no harm at all.' But there is such a thing as being too generous in expressing a judgment impulsively, and Oak added with a more appreciative sense of all the circumstances – 'Well, I am not quite certain it was no harm.'

'Indeed, I hadn't time to think before starting whether I wanted to marry or not, for you'd have been gone over the hill.'

'Come,' said Gabriel, freshening again; 'think a minute or two. I'll wait a while, Miss Everdene. Will you marry me? Do, Bathsheba. I love you far more than common!'

'I'll try to think,' she observed rather more timorously; 'if I can think out of doors; my mind spreads away so.'

'But you can give a guess.'

'Then give me time.' Bathsheba looked thoughtfully into the distance, away from the direction in which Gabriel stood.

'I can make you happy,' said he to the back of her head, across the bush. 'You shall have a piano in a year or two – farmers' wives are getting to have pianos now – and I'll practise up the flute right well to play with you in the evenings.'

'Yes; I should like that.'

'And have one of those little ten-pound gigs for market – and nice flowers, and birds – cocks and hens I mean, because they be useful,' continued Gabriel, feeling balanced between poetry and practicality.

'I should like it very much.'

'And a frame for cucumbers – like a gentleman and lady.'

'Yes.'

'And when the wedding was over, we'd have it put in the newspaper list of marriages.'

'Dearly I should like that!'

'And the babies in the births – every man jack of 'em! And at home by the fire, whenever you look up, there I shall be – and whenever I look up, there will be you.'

'Wait, wait, and don't be improper!'

Her countenance fell, and she was silent awhile. He regarded the red berries between them over and over again, to such an extent that holly seemed in his after life to be a cypher signifying a proposal of marriage. Bathsheba decisively turned to him.

'No; 'tis no use,' she said. 'I don't want to marry you.'

'Try.'

'I've tried hard all the time I've been thinking; for a marriage would be very nice in one sense. People would talk about me and think I had won my battle, and I should feel triumphant, and all that. But a husband—'

'Well!'

'Why, he'd always be there, as you say; whenever I looked up, there he'd be.'

'Of course he would – I, that is.'

'Well, what I mean is that I shouldn't mind being a bride at a wedding, if I could be one without having a husband. But since a woman can't show off in that way by herself, I shan't marry – at least yet.'

'That's a terrible wooden story!'

At this criticism of her statement Bath-sheba made an addition to her dignity by a slight sweep away from him.

'Upon my heart and soul I don't know what a maid can say stupider than that,' said Oak. 'But dearest,' he continued in a palliative voice, 'don't be like it!' Oak sighed a deep honest sigh – none the less so in that, being like the sigh of a pine plantation, it was rather noticeable as a disturbance of the atmosphere. 'Why won't you have me?' he appealed, creeping round the holly to reach her side.

'I cannot,' she said, retreating.

'But why?' he persisted, standing still at last in despair of ever reaching her, and facing over the bush.

'Because I don't love you.'

'Yes, but—'

She contracted a yawn to an inoffensive smallness, so that it was hardly ill-mannered at all. 'I don't love you,' she said.

'But I love you – and, as for myself, I am content to be liked.'

'O Mr Oak – that's very fine! You'd get to despise me.'

'Never,' said Mr Oak, so earnestly that he seemed to be coming, by the force of his words, straight through the bush and into her arms. 'I shall do one thing in this life – one thing certain – that is, love you, and long for you, and *keep wanting you* till I die.' His voice had a genuine pathos now, and his large brown hands perceptibly trembled.

'It seems dreadfully wrong not to have you when you feel so much!' she said with a little distress, and looking hopelessly around for some means of escape from her moral dilemma. 'How I wish I hadn't run after you!' However, she seemed to have a short cut for getting back to cheerfulness and set her face to signify archness. 'It wouldn't do, Mr Oak. I want somebody to tame me; I am too independent; and you would never be able to, I know.'

Oak cast his eyes down the field in a way implying that it was useless to attempt argument.

'Mr Oak,' she said, with luminous distinctness and common sense, 'you are better off than I. I have hardly a penny in the world – I am staying with my aunt for my bare sustenance. I am better educated than you – and I don't love you a bit: that's my side of the case. Now yours: you are a farmer just beginning, and you ought in common prudence, if you marry at all (which you should certainly not think of doing at present) to marry a woman with money, who would stock a larger farm for you than you have now.'

Gabriel looked at her with a little surprise and much admiration.

'That's the very thing I had been thinking myself!' he naïvely said.

Farmer Oak had one-and-a-half Christian characteristics too many to succeed with Bathsheba: his humility, and a superfluous moiety of honesty. Bathsheba was decidedly disconcerted.

'Well, then, why did you come and disturb me?' she said, almost angrily, if not quite, an enlarging red spot rising in each cheek.

'I can't do what I think would be – would be —'

'Right?'

'No: wise.'

'You have made an admission *now*, Mr Oak,' she exclaimed with even more hauteur, and rocking her head disdainfully. 'After that, do you think I could marry you? Not if I know it.'

He broke in passionately: 'But don't mistake me like that! Because I am open enough to own what every man in my shoes would have thought of, you make your colours come up your face and get crabbed with me. That about you not being good enough for me is nonsense. You speak like a lady – all the parish notice it, and your uncle at Weatherbury is, I've heerd, a large farmer – much larger than ever I shall be. May I call in the evening, or will you walk along with me o' Sundays? I don't want you to make up your mind at once, if you'd rather not.'

'No – no – I cannot. Don't press me any more – don't. I don't love you – so 'twould be ridiculous,' she said, with a laugh.

No man likes to see his emotions the sport of a merry-go-round of skittishness. 'Very well,' said Oak firmly, with the bearing of one who was going to give his days and nights to Ecclesiastes for ever. 'Then I'll ask you no more.'

Thomas Hardy, *Far From the Madding Crowd*

Mergers and Acquisitions

NEVER marry for money, ye'll borrow it cheaper.

Old Scottish saying

The financial aspect of marriage prior to this century, and the elaborate detail with which it was worked out between the parties, seems mercenary by today's standards, to the extent of nullifying the sentiment that brings two people to the altar in the first place. But to families whose income derived from the land they owned, leased, rented or farmed, transactions concerning the division of such property – either as inheritance or 'portions' paid in marriage – were vital for the livelihood of the extant family and for members of its future generations.

It is common to find in almost all societies in the world dependent on land, goods and the money to provide both, a form of transfer of possessions linked to marriage, and it is most usually coupled with arranged marriage; the general feeling being that where property and finances were concerned matters were best left to the parents. The preoccupation since Roman times, at least, with the exchange of property, possessions and money at marriage is related to several factors, the most important being that the family was viewed as a social tool and therefore the sons and daughters were used, upon marriage, to increase the power base of the family in society. The family hierarchy favoured the eldest son and it was only in the nineteenth century that children began to be treated in the same way regardless of their sex or birth order. Wealthy families would also choose the time of marriage to settle inheritances on their children – both boys and girls – so that weddings were viewed as crucial times for restructuring the family's finances.

The size and importance of dowries and portions was also connected to the fact that people died young and a woman, particularly, might expect to marry twice in her life. Given that she was likely to have children by both husbands, it was essential that the children from the first marriage should not be disinherited and that sufficient funds be set aside to accommodate their marriage plans. Portions for stepchildren were often

Weddings gave people the opportunity to show off their wealth. *The Wedding Party* by Carlf Herpfer.

The Marriage Contract (Anon.): A source of great discussion and often dispute.

settled at the time of the second marriage and played an important part in the marriage being accepted by the kin of the wife and children.

In former times, before a banking system such as the one available to us today was in existence, families looked to each other to supply money, credit and loans. This closed family ties in a way which is quite unrecognizable to us now. Without job availability, pension plans and money from the social services departments, people borrowed from a network of relatives, thus becoming indebted to them often for many years. Money was lent out at interest, and cash and property were given by parents to trustees to manage on behalf of sons and daughters until they became of marriageable age.

The word 'dowry' is confusing because it used to mean the same as a dower, which represents the portion to which a widow was entitled from her deceased husband's estate. The word 'dowry', as we think of it now, is the money or property a bride brings to her groom at the time of the marriage. But the dowry has co-existed with various other forms of property and monetary exchange, such as the dower or portion, and the morning gift (a bridegift from the groom to the bride and paid to her the morning after the marriage in compensation for the surrender of her virginity). Under the Germanic marital customs this was known as the *'morgengabe'*, or 'morning gift', and in the Anglo-Saxon period as the *'morgengifu'*. In both periods the payment was usually in the form of land or money, sometimes jewellery.

Bridewealth, sometimes known as bridepiece, was paid to the father of the bride or

In most marriage contracts the bride and groom were not consulted. *The Marriage Contract* by A. Bosse.

to her kinsmen by the groom or his family, in other words a kind of 'bride-purchase', the idea behind which was a form of compensation for the loss of a daughter. Often, a token of the total price, known as the 'arrha', was paid to the family in advance, when the betrothal was announced, as a form of intent to complete the transaction. It bound both families to each other and to the engagement. The bridepurchases (*'coemptio'*, in Latin) was a feature of Barbarian marriages and historians have suggested that this type of transaction was prevalent during periods when there was a shortage of women.

The direction of the dowry (gift from bride to groom or bride's parents to groom) and the morning gift (gift from husband to wife on the morning after the marriage had been consummated) have not changed. The dower, on the other hand was originally a gift from groom to bride's parents or guardian and suggests a form of bridepurchase common in the Roman and early Germanic period. It appears to have been firmly established by early medieval times as a form of settlement by the parents of the groom to the bride and came to be known as a 'portion'. 'Portion' is a confusing word, because it also means a dowry (i.e. the contribution in cash, movable goods and immovable goods, such as land and buildings) that a bride brings to her marriage and known as her 'marriage portion' and a part of her parent's estate (to which she is entitled either during their lifetimes or after their deaths) which could be considered as part of her marriage portion. Thus a portion was both and separately a marriage gift and an expected gift. From this word 'portion' evolved the 'jointure' or 'widow's portion' which was a sum of money, or land, settled on the bride by the parents of the groom so that she would have financial independence should her husband die young. As we have seen, certain restrictions were put upon the dower: often the wife was able to make use of the land only until the eldest son of the marriage reached his majority when the land would pass to him. This was a direct result of the change in sentiment about the family and its inheritors, and the reign of primogeniture. If there were no children from the marriage, the land was given back to the husband's kinsmen. This was also the case if the woman married for the second time. Common law, which was incorporated into the Magna Carta of 1215, regulated many of the laws regarding widows and their rights.

Dowries, jointures, portions and gifts were all part of a complex rearrangement of family finances carried out between the betrothal and the wedding. We have seen that until fairly recently in our history the betrothal was, arguably, the most important aspect of the nuptials, when the families of the couple, in front of witnesses, agreed to the terms of the marriage and a pledge was given, either in writing or by the exchange of rings, and in some instances money and property was exchanged. With the Church's increasing involvement in marriage from the eleventh century it was common practice to announce the dower and dowry at the church doorway. The idea behind this practice was the publication

Bridesmaids learned what would be expected of them on their wedding days. *Wedding in Aragon* by Juan Pablo Salinas.

of the transaction to the general populace, any member of which could take issue with the parents if he felt that the property being exchanged was inadequate or if in fact the exchange was illegal, the property belonging to someone else.

The history of the dowry (the gift from the father or family of the bride to the groom or his kinsmen) is directly related to that of the bridepurchase. When the bridepurchase was in common usage, the dowry played a smaller role and vice versa. In periods of land shortage parents could not expect to receive large endowments for their daughters, and meeting the needs of the time they provided their daughters with dowries to attract husbands.

When a suitor presented himself, or a son declared his desire to marry, parents would ask themselves where the young couple would live, and from what source would they derive an income. If they were of the appropriate class they had to keep servants and, if so, how many, and how were they to be paid? Would the dowry and the young man's situation be sufficient to provide settlements for the daughters born from the marriage so that they might, in turn, be provided with dowries? Could the father provide widows' jointures for his sons' wives? These were the most pressing problems that occupied the mind of a parent with children of marriageable age.

In his book *Marriage and Love in England, 1300–1840,* Alan MacFarlane writes:

> In order to set up a successful marriage in the years between the fifteenth and nineteenth centuries, it was felt necessary to have four types of asset. First, one needed somewhere to live – preferably, as we have seen, a house of one's own. Secondly, it was necessary to have the furnishings for house and body: furniture, cooking utensils, bedding and clothes. Thirdly, it was essential to have prospects of an assured income over the years ahead. This could take numerous forms: income from land, interest from investments, a profession or trade. In some of these activities it was necessary to have the stock and tools with which to derive the income. Finally, it was advisable to have some ready cash – to cover the initial costs, to help with the early expensive years of child-rearing, and in case of accident and sickness.

MacFarlane goes on to point out that under the English system the wife provided two of the four necessities with her portion: the furniture and furnishings, and the cash.

So, what exactly was a dowry? Traditionally, a dowry has always been considered to be land or money, or both. Acreage, a farm, a vineyard, or, for the very wealthy, buildings such as a manor or castle. Whatever it was came under the husband's jurisdiction during the marriage. For the less wealthy, the dowry could be grain, farm animals or farm equipment, carts and vessels. As well as furniture, tables, stools, benches, chests and other household goods, such as cooking utensils, hooks, bowls, spits, vinegar barrels, knives, plates, cups, salt cellars, candlesticks and items made of silver, the dowry might also include table linens, bed canopies and furnishings, blankets, sheets, coverlets and cushions, and the value of many items were often subtracted from the cash value of the dowry, as the couple would not have to purchase them to set up home. In the words of Olwen H. Hufton in *Marriage and Society,* the materials and cooking utensils brought by the bride to her marriage, in many cases serving as a dowry, were expected to last through marriage and might

Guests took presents to the bride's home before the wedding day. *Marriage in the Country: Presenting Presents* by A. Bosse.

make a second appearance in the notarial records when death removed the last partner. But they would be differently qualified – *un chétif lit, du mauvais linge, de vieux outils, tous usés* – all worn out. Dearly purchased by the young in terms of human effort, carefully amassed to cope with the problems of parenthood, pawned or sold in hours of need, these vestiges remained to bear witness to a lifetime's struggle, shabby, yet eloquent relics of the passage of a marriage.

After the birth of a daughter, a mother would start collecting household goods to form part of the girl's dowry. In some parts of France trees were cut down after the birth of a girl and a dowry armoire was made, for which the mother would accumulate linens and furnishings. Typically, the armoire would be carved in a manner appropriate to the status of the family.

Dower furniture was evident in Renaissance Italy where the *cassone* or dower chest was in popular use. The concept spread to cabinet-makers in Germany, Switzerland, France and Holland and was taken with the Dutch and German settlers to America. Couples often had a piece of furniture, usually an armoire (a *kast* or *schrank* in Germany and Holland), made for them to commemorate their wedding. Wardrobes and cupboards such as these would be carved with symbols which expressed luck and happiness to the married pair, such as hearts, birds, the tree of life, tulips and crowns. The names of the husband and wife would appear along with the date of their marriage.

Under English law the husband was entitled to do whatsoever he chose with his wife's dowry as long as he maintained her in a manner to which she was accustomed. He did not, however, have rights over her clothing or personal possessions. The goods and chattels, cash, leases, rents etc, which the bride brought with her could therefore be used to establish the eldest son, pay the dowries of the daughters or pay off debts. In most cases under the system of primogeniture, which became common not only with the aristocracy but also with the peasants, the father willed his wife's dowry to his son along with the rest of his estate.

The custom of the eldest son being the sole inheritor of his father's estate (primogeniture), which was established in the Middle Ages, created problems for his siblings, for, in the event of the death of the father, his sisters looked to their eldest brother to provide them with a sufficient dowry to attract a suitor. For female members of the aristocracy and even the 'middling' classes, being unable to provide a dowry for oneself meant greater dependency on the menfolk of the family – an unenviable position for women that existed for centuries. In earlier times, when the feudal system was the foundation of society, daughters were given to knights and in the absence of a dowry, the lord would demand fewer services from his son-in-law.

For medieval women of the peasant class a different option was available. A young woman wishing to marry early on in life could do so, with her parent's permission, but her dowry would not be significant because it would take her father a great number of working years to provide for all his children. By general rule, the later women married the more likely they were to bring their new husbands a larger dowry. In poor societies – arranged marriages did not exist, as it would not have been possible to instruct a girl who had been self-sufficient and working since the age of twelve as to whom she would marry. Nonetheless girls still saved and accumulated possessions to form dowries, in the hope that rather than a man of their own standing they might attract a wealthier man or an ambitious one who would use her dowry to set themselves up in business.

In medieval times, fathers of the bride not only supplied the dowry but paid the 'merchet', a kind of land tax paid to the lord for the transfer of property held by his free peasants on the occasion of their marriage, or paid by unfree peasants. However, historical research suggests that it was not paid by all peasants – many would not be able to raise a dowry – and that the actual sum was based on the size of the dowry, and whether or not the marriage took place outside the manor. There is also historical evidence that women themselves paid the merchet to the lord when they wished to marry a man outside the manor. There was much dispute over the payment of the merchet and it was not always received by the lord in monetary value: grain was also used. There is a strong suggestion here that these were marriages of choice, with women marrying whom they pleased. Certainly, a woman who could earn money had a right to save sufficient funds to marry the man of her choice. If her father had not provided for her, she was under no obligation to seek his consent to the union.

The size of the dowry was left to the parties involved. Obviously, the wealthier the parents of the bride the larger the dowry would be, but it might not be paid all at once.

All her worldly goods being moved to her new home. *The Highland Bride's Departure* by Jacob Thompson.

In the eighteenth century, when large dowries were common among the aristocracy, many dowries were paid out over a number of years after a downpayment had been received by the groom's family at the time of the marriage.

The sources of dowries (that is, where the money came from) are as varied as the sizes of the wedding gifts. Other than an inheritance from her parents, a girl might receive a gift from a relative, an uncle on the father's side, or a grandfather. Anything from a few shillings to ten pounds was not uncommon amongst ordinary people. (A philanthropic widow in England was recorded as having left sixpence to every maiden in her village.) Other than wages, servants also received funds from their masters on their weddings which contributed to their dowries. The village community, neighbours and friends might group together to be able to provide a small dowry.

Amongst the aristocracy, a girl might look to an aunt for her dowry, or a grandmother. In 1731 Lady Diana Spencer married John Russell, younger brother of the third Duke of Bedford, with a dowry of £30,000 which was provided by her grandmother Sarah, Duchess of Marlborough. King Henry VIII provided not only a dowry for one of his mistresses, Elizabeth Blount, but also a husband. Upon her marriage to Gilbert Talboys, the king granted her the manor of Rokeby in Warwickshire.

Many women would sell off lands they brought with them to the marriage, with their husband's permission, in order to provide their daughters with a dowry. Land itself in Europe before the Plague was at such a premium that one acre would secure a girl a husband.

If parents were sensible they invested wisely the money intended for dowries. Although many daughters might not live to see adulthood, prudent parents nonetheless would take the necessary steps to provide dowries. Ffeoffees or trustees were often appointed to manage the monies or trusts in the event of the death of the father and mother. However, years of planning could not prevent disaster striking. Five of the six daughters of Sir Ralph Verney were not the only victims of the Civil War in England that made their portions inaccessible. These financial problems so reduced the girls' chances of good alliances that they were forced to accept inferior marriages. Land that could not be sold because it was in dispute over ownership hardly a suitable component of a marriage portion; neither were debt-encumbered properties, which were common enough amongst the nobility. The Wandesford's family property was sequestered during the Civil War and the daughter, Alice, was married off at the age of fifteen in an arrangement that promised that the uncle of the groom was to retrieve the property. Alice herself knew nothing of the deal until the contract had been made.

One obvious solution to the problem of raising dowries was to marry off the eldest son well and use the portion received from the family of his wife to dower his remaining sisters. The nobility, often impoverished by the slowness with which they were reimbursed for services rendered to the king and by their own extravagant lifestyle, were forced to look outside their own ranks for brides. This is what happened in 1694 to the Marquis de Grignan, Louis-Provence d'Adhémar de Monteil, eldest son of the Count and Countess de Grignan, who was married off to the daughter of a wealthy tax-farmer to prevent his family from bankruptcy. Anne-Marguerite de Saint-Amans brought with her a dowry of 400,000 livres, 300,000 of which came in cash and were used to pay off the Count's debts, principally to his youngest daughter by his first wife, now Madame de Vibraye, who demanded the bequest left to her from her mother's will. It was not the first time the Count de Grignan had known a financial crisis: at his own marriage to Françoise-Marguerite de Sévigné in 1668, 180,000 of the 200,000 livres cash due on the eve of the nuptials were used to pay off the Count's most pressing debts.

In the sixteenth century the Prioress of Littlemore Priory sold off valuable convent artefacts in order to be able to provide a dowry for her illegitimate daughter.

Perhaps the most curious source for a dowry is that known as the Poydras Dowry. Julien Lalande Poydras was born in 1746 in Nantes, France. As a young man he met the girl he wanted to marry but because she was the daughter of a pauper the nuptials could not take place. Poydras joined the French navy and found himself in Louisiana in 1768, where he settled, and within years he had amassed a fortune comprising five cotton plantations, several herds of cattle and over one thousand slaves. He never married, and in order to ensure that no other man should find himself in a situation of being unable to marry the woman of his choice for lack of a dowry, he left $30,000 in his will to the parish of West Baton Rouge. The money was to be invested and the interest divided annually among brides who have lived in the parish for at least five years. The Poydras Dowry is still paying brides today – although the meagre sum could not amount to a dowry. How was Poydras to know that 168 years after his death women would no longer require dowries?

In more recent years the custom and practice of providing dowries and jointures has died out, although many marriages contain nuptial agreements. During the First World War William Waldorf gave Lady Violet, the wife of his son, John Jacob Astor, $30,000 a year for life in addition to the $4,000,000 she had received on her wedding day.

Dowries do not fit into a free-choice society when people choose to marry for love, when both parties work or when one party earns enough to support both, when private and state pensions are available to those surviving to old age. Portions are not necessary when the law gives the wife rights to her husband's estate after his death. While some forms of marriage settlements were still in practice amongst wealthy landowners in the early part of this century, for the majority the practice of dowering daughters was no longer a financial necessity. A daughter who married of her own free will might ask her father's permission, and accept a gift upon her marriage, but neither her husband nor her father would expect to exchange money or lands on the wedding day.

In the past dowries have been the subject of dramatic interest. In Shakespeare's *Measure for Measure*, Mariana, whose love was rejected when her suitor discovered that her dowry had been lost at sea, was one of the Victorian era's most popular figures, that of the spurned lover. But consider the fate of the poor woman who was intending to marry James Greenacre in the early nineteenth century. Greenacre was hung in 1837 for the murder of the woman; on discovering she had no money he dismembered her body and distributed it around London.

Exotic bridal clothes for the *Sheriff's Daughter in Tangiers,* painted by José Tapiro y Baro in the nineteenth century.

Plans and Preparations

Advent marriage both deny,
But Hilary gives thee liberty;
Septuagesima says thee nay,
Eight days from Easter says you may;
Rogation bids thee to contain,
But Trinity sets thee free again.

Anon.

The long engagement, the stuff of Victorian romantic novels, represented Victorian ideas of devotion – keeping the fires of love and the flame of duty burning over long years of chaperoned visits – but it had in fact, almost no precedent in history. It related only to a time when children were betrothed at the age of seven, or younger, but not actually married until puberty and was a remote reflection of the distant kind of love associated with chivalry. In spite of the enormous changes in the business of getting married over the centuries, the engagement – or the time between betrothal and the nuptial ceremony – has more or less stayed the same at six months to two years, with the most usual time being one year. That is not to say that many people did not meet and marry within a shorter period of time, the engagement announcement preceding the wedding notice by only a few weeks; but it was usual, in every century, for the engagement to be stretched out over months.

——————— ♡ ———————

GOOD nature, and Evenness of Temper, will give you an easie Companion for Life; Virtue and good Sense an agreeable Friend; Love and Constancy, a good Wife or Husband.

Anon.

——————— ♡ ———————

The length of an engagement was determined usually by all kinds of practical reasons. Either parents, or the bride and groom themselves, needed time to save up sufficient funds not only to pay for the wedding but also to start a home. It was quite common for middle-class men to wait until they had reached a comfortable situation in life, perhaps by the time they were in their mid-thirties, and had a home of their own, or at least a regular job which provided them with money for rent, before they would begin to search for a wife. Young couples waiting for a tenancy might delay the marriage until it became available, for most young couples preferred to live on their own rather than have to live in the home of one or other set of parents, and while the wedding gifts in the form of furniture and household goods might assist them, a home of their own was still top priority.

When dowries were necessary aspects of marriage, people needed time to collect debts and outstanding loans and rearrange finances and property transfers in order to have the cash, or property titles, available at the time of the wedding. All this had to be done in a society where the credit system was largely extended not through a bank but through a complicated network of family alliances. Any delay on the part of the parent in providing the marriage portion could postpone the wedding ceremony.

From a social aspect, the length of the engagement gave people the time to plan a wedding, invite the guests – many of whom might live some distance away – and prepare the bride, getting her trousseau and wedding clothes ready, just as a wedding is planned today.

THERE is perhaps no time when the rules of etiquette need to be so strictly observed as during the period between betrothal and marriage. All the world loves a lover, but this does not keep the world from watching closely and condemning any breach of good manners, especially on the part of the young lady.

Lillian Eichler, *A New Book of Etiquette*, 1936

BRIDAL SETS.
Be sure to give bust measure.

$4.35

Undoubtedly the wedding dress was the most important part of the trousseau – the outfits, dresses, coats, lingerie and personal articles the bride brought to her marriage – and one can safely imagine that for people of earlier centuries as much time, effort and relative amount of money went into the wedding dress as it does today. Poorer people, who today might extend credit to pay for a lavish wedding, including an expensive dress, were unable to do this. A bride would have worn her best dress, perhaps the one she wore to church on Sundays, with some additional trimming. This dress would have been made of as costly a material as the family could afford, and of a light colour, pale yellow or blue, rose or lilac, until the vogue for white weddings filtered down to even the poorest people. Being cheaper fabrics than light colours

A great deal of time, money and effort was put into making the wedding dress which, after being worn once, was stored away often for ever. *The Wedding Dress* by George Godwin Kilburne.

russet brown and even grey were colours worn by poor people and the wedding dress may simply have been a new dress serviceable afterwards. These were also the colours favoured by deeply religious brides who felt that the pastel shades reflected an unnecessary frivolity.

Many wedding dresses were kept and never worn again; others were worn on special occasions, and there was even a vogue in the nineteenth century for brides to wear their wedding dresses to dinner parties held after the wedding.

Brides today select their bouquets, or nosegays and posies as they were once called, in colours that correspond with the trimmings on their wedding dresses, which are invariably white or cream. It may come as a surprise to many people to know that the white wedding is largely a production of the nineteenth century. That is not to say that prior to then people were not married in white – the wearing of white actually began in the mid-eighteenth century – but the prevalence of white weddings belongs firmly to nineteenth century traditions which stressed the purity and virginity of the bride as being a significant feature of the wedding ceremony.

Unfortunately, few written details of what 'the bride wore' have survived and most of the information available to us dates from the eighteenth and nineteenth centuries, with the exception of royal weddings which were usually documented.

BRIDAL DRESS

PETTICOAT of white satin of a lustrous kind: at the hem a pleating of thick white gauze. The over-skirt of soft silk gauze, drawn up in four places to form a drapery of *festoons,* which is thickly set with pear-shaped pearls. To cover these gatherings bows and spaces of white satin ribbon are used. The back of this over-skirt falls in full pleats of satin, ending in a short train.

The bodice of the same material as the skirt, is full and thickly pearled.

The sleeves are full to the elbow of the rich material, and also pearled. From the elbow to the wrist the sleeves are of white satin, fastened with pearl and silver bangles looped together in a mass; they do not separate. Corset of white satin. The tulle veil is fastened with a bunch of orange blossom.

The whole dress, plain and made up patterns, 5s.

Fashions and Fancies.

Everything for the Bride. It would be almost impossible to keep one's thoughts from straying to the absorbing subject of bridal array this week, and the sketches on this page are offered as a suggestion to those who are soon to follow the royal example. Silver lace and silver embroidery play an important part in many fashionable wedding gowns, and the lovely dress shown here is of white charmeuse, decorated in this way. Victorian, Egyptian, and strictly modern styles share the honours where bridal gowns are concerned this spring, and a departure from the conventional complete white

The simpler the arrangement of the veil, the greater the charm.

toilette is the new idea of using only gold tissue and gold lace. Certainly the all-gold bride looks very effective, and throws the bridegroom even more into the shade than usual !

Bouquet-Making as an Art. Small children are undoubtedly the most ornamental attendants for the bride, and one of the only drawbacks to very small girls as bridesmaids is that they have such an unfortunate knack of either dropping their bouquets altogether at the wrong moment, or, at any rate, of letting slip some of the flowers. Practical fashion

An idea for small bridesmaids : flower-filled baskets of white wistaria wood.

…as surmounted the difficulty by introducing the bridesmaid's basket, which tiny folk can manage far more easily than a bouquet. Goodyear, of the Royal Arcade, Old Bond Street, is the artist in flower arrangement who is responsible for the lovely bride's bouquet. Those exquisite Mollie Charman-Crawford roses are used, and with them are lilies of the valley, while on the long tulle streamers which hold the flowers are scattered, as though by a careless hand, stray lily-of-the-valley sprays.

Real Butterflies.

The latest idea in connection with bouquets is to mount real English butterflies on the flowers they actually visit. This wonderful florist would never dream of posing them on tulips or bluebells, for these flowers are not in bloom in the butterfly season. Bridesmaids' favours are coming into their own again, and so are the old-fashioned bouquets which were once an indispensable part of a coachman's livery. Court bouquets can be had from 17s. 6d. each.

The Wedding Cake.

The general verdict on the beautiful wedding cake prepared by McVitie

A profusion of roses and lilies of the valley. Sprays of the latter are scattered over the tulle streamers.

and Price for the marriage of Princess Mary and Viscount Lascelles was that it was far too perfect a piece of workmanship to submit to the indignity of being eaten. The same applies to the really wonderful cake that these world-famous biscuit-manufacturers have contributed to the event of the week. It is well worthy of its predecessor, and stands 9 ft. in height, yet, in spite of its weight, which is approximately 800 lb., it is almost fairy-like in the delicacy of its construction. Tier after tier, each decorated in a different manner, rise upwards in a long, tapering design to the silver bowl at the summit, where little cupids stand distributing flowers. The bowl itself is of repoussé work, showing the new combined coat of arms, and it holds a magnificent bouquet of roses, lilies of the valley, and white orchids tipped with mauve. Sugar lace is the chief feature of the decoration. E. A. R.

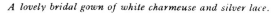

A lovely bridal gown of white charmeuse and silver lace.

Brocade shoes for the bride.

THE BRIDAL ROBE

THE white robe made for the nuptials of the Royal bride was not ready till last week, as the Spitalfields looms could not produce so elaborate a brocade at any rapid rate. The design of the dress is given below. The long train was perfectly plain, and the front of the dress was of white satin, with three tiny flounces edged with silver at the bottom. The fine old Honiton point lace in which her mother, H.R.H. Princess Mary, Duchess of Teck, was married, was arranged in three flounces just above, and long trails of orange-blossom, with buds and foliage, were carried down on either side of the flounced space. Two more trails were brought across from the sides at a short distance below the hips, lightly tied together in the centre, where there was a little droop, and then fell to the edge of the dress. The long-pointed bodice was made of the white and silver brocade, and some more of the Duchess of Teck's Honiton trimmed the top of the bodice and formed the upper part of the sleeve. A small wreath of orange-blossom was carried all the way round the bust, with a little bouquet on each shoulder, and a larger one in the centre, with which a little white heather was mingled. Princess May also wore her mother's Honiton lace veil, floating backwards, and leaving her face full in view. It was secured with diamond pins, the largest of which was Her Majesty's present, and a small wreath of orange-blossom was placed on the hair. The dress was made by Mesdames Linton and Curtis, of 16, Albermarle Street, S.W.

The Graphic, Royal Wedding Number,
10 July 1893

When Princess Sophia Friederika Augusta of Anhalt-Zerbst, who had become Grand Duchess Yecatarina Alexievna (Catherine the Great), married Grand Duke Peter Feodorovich on 21 August 1745, she wore a dress of 'silver moiré embroidered in silver on all the hems and of a terrific weight'. It was the weight of the bride that was commented on at the wedding of Princess Charlotte to Prince Leopold of Saxe-Coburg-Saalfeld on 2 May 1816. Her wedding dress comprised of layers and layers of a fabric sewn with silver metallic thread, embroidered with patterns of shells and bouquets at the borders. The dress had many frills and trimmings and was cut full below the high bodice which served to emphasize the Princess's large shape. Princess Victoria, 'Vicky', the Princess Royal (daughter of Queen Victoria), wore white moiré trimmed with Honiton lace at her wedding on 25 January 1858 at the Chapel Royal, St James's. Her bridal veil was fastened by white roses. Her sister-in-law, Princess Alexandra of Denmark, on her marriage to Prince Edward (later King Edward VII) on 10 March 1863, wore an 'English made dress of silver tissue, and Honiton lace in a pattern of roses, shamrocks and thistles. The skirt was draped with garlands of orange blossoms, more flowers twisted with diamonds in her hair.'

Silk, which was often used for wedding dresses, is available in a variety of weights

Putting together a trousseau could take a great deal of time and money. *Selecting the Trousseau*
by Eugene von de Blaas.

type of silk is specified. To a certain extent this applies to lace as well, although it is much easier to find references to Honiton, Brussels or Valenciennes lace. Wedding dresses themselves, which tend to be kept within families for sentimental reasons, tell their own story, but one dress does not explain a vogue. Researchers have discovered that stylistically wedding dresses tended to follow the fashions of the day more closely than today when a bride can choose from the fashions of almost one thousand years for the style of her wedding dress. That is not to say that a bride of the 1890s, for instance, might not choose an Elizabethan style ruff for the neckline of her dress; but wedding dresses of the nineteenth century were made with stays and to accommodate corsets, an essential part of dress at the time, while post-First World War dresses did not have stays and reflected the slim-line fashions of the twenties and thirties.

Fashions in wedding dresses changed much more slowly than they do today, largely because so many were handmade and not mass-produced. Lace was the predominate feature of wedding dresses in the eighteenth and nineteenth centuries. Expensive gowns were adorned with hand-made lace, while less expensive models used cheaper, machine-made lace for trimming or the basic design of the dress. Queen Victoria wore Honiton lace, which originates from Devon in England, at her wedding in 1839 and the lace became a fashionable feature for wedding dresses for the rest of the nineteenth century. Valenciennes, Brussels and Honiton lace were especially popular for veils during the nineteenth century. By the twentieth century lace was being used far less – becoming instead a permanent feature on lingerie – and short veils were being worn on hats rather than long veils secured to a garland or tiara. Although lace was generally seen less in this century, Miss Grace Kelly of Philadelphia used 320 yards of Valenciennes lace in her wedding dress on her marriage in 1956 to Prince Rainier of Monaco.

Another feature of wedding dresses of the nineteenth century that survived, in limited fashion, until the Second World War, was the court train. This popularity was interrupted only by the crinoline, which did not lend itself easily to a train. Trains varied enormously in length. The couturier Worth developed a particularly long train for the bustled bride, and trains were also seen on 'going-away' clothes and the walking dresses, in which one took a stroll or promenade, of the trousseau.

Towards the end of the nineteenth century colours for wedding dresses changed. As well as white, they were made in mauve, lilac, pale grey, ivory and a colour called candlelight. Mauve and lilac were the result of the discovery of aniline dyes made from indigo in the 1850s. Until this time animal and vegetable dyes had been used to colour fabrics. In the early twentieth century off-white, *café au lait* and cream were popular colours.

The Victorian bustle gave way to the high-necked, leg-of-mutton-sleeved Edwardian gown, which in turn evolved into the slimmer Princess line with long inset panels, and the *robes de style* of the early twentieth century. Then came the long tube dress over a skirt, which became the train of the 1920s, followed by the sheaths of the 1930s. In the post-war era of the New Look, women were married in suits, their waists nipped in by boning and their skirts short and full with stiff petticoats. Navy blue, pink and a host of colours previously unassociated with wedding dresses were seen as the exigencies of the Second World War had forced people to rethink wedding clothes.

The traditional slippers worn by brides became shoes, often made of soft fabric, luxuriously patterned, embroidered or appliquéd. Gloves, which were essential parts of dress, were seen less after the 1950s as they were generally excluded from fashion itself.

More emphasis was placed in the past on jewellery than it is today, although no specific jewels were recommended for the bride. She might wear earrings or a parure, and the bride who had no jewellery of her own might borrow some from the parish priest, who kept a small collection of jewellery which had been donated to the church. Wealthy brides during the late nineteenth and early twentieth centuries wore tiaras which are rarely seen today. The American heiress Anna Gould, on her marriage to Count Boniface de Castellane in New York on 4 March 1895, wore a tiara of emeralds, pearls, diamonds and rubies worth $40,000. Her husband designed her wedding dress, which was made of white satin and old lace. The bridal veil was a gift from the Marquise de Castellane, an old point lace secured with clusters of lily of the valley her four bridesmaids were dressed in white cloth, trimmed with sable.

Another trimming, which has changed little, is the use of seed pearls, which can still be found sewn extensively on to wedding dresses today. Velvet and fur, the latter used widely in medieval times, have declined in popularity. Velvet was often seen in the nineteenth century in the going-away clothes of the bride.

The size of a bride's trousseau (the word means *trusse* or little bundle of household items) varied: the wealthier the parents, the larger the trousseau with which a bride could start her life as a married woman. In 1936 the *New Book of Etiquette* recommended the following:

At least one smart suit with an appropriate hat
Several blouses suitable to be worn with this suit
A top-coat or wrap
An evening wrap
Three or four afternoon dresses
Three dinner dresses suitable also for semi-formal evening occasions
At least two evening dresses
One or two tea gowns
Hats appropriate for these clothes
Shoes suitable for walking, evening wear, and use with afternoon and dinner dresses
Gloves suitable for the various costumes
One or two dozen pairs of stockings, including those for evening and sport use
Sweater and skirt outfits for use in the country
Handkerchiefs and other accessories
At least one bathrobe
Two négligés
Six to twelve chemises or slips
Six to twelve under sets (panties and brassières)
Six to twelve nightgowns
Three breakfast coats
A pair of bedroom slippers or mules.

THE BRIDE'S TROUSSEAU

THE Duchess of Teck's patriotic determination that her daughter's trousseau should be entirely of English, Scotch, and Irish manufactures did credit alike to her heart and head. The spending of money in the United Kingdom is the great thing, and, as a consequence, fashion follows suit, and British manufactures become the rage. Orders for some lovely dinner-gowns were given to Mrs Sims, of Dublin. Mr Alfred Manning, Dublin, also had some commissions, notably for Irish lace, and also for dresses. He made one of the smartest yachting gowns ever seen afloat.

Messrs Redfern over and above the bride's travelling-gown made her some very pretty coats and dresses, a yachting-gown, a white serge three-quarter shirt and jacket, half a dozen silk blouses, and some dainty millinery. Messrs Scott Adie, of the Royal Clan Tartan Warehouse, Regent Street, made a Hume jacket, an Abergeldie coat, Cawdor cape, and several other good and useful garments especially suitable for a lady who spends much time in the open air, and they will make up the homespuns and other woollen materials bought by the Duchess of Teck when she opened the sale of the Scottish Industries at Mr Astor's house in Carlton House Terrace.

Some most beautiful Devonshire lace was supplied for Princess May's trousseau by Miss Herbert, the successor of old Mrs Treadwin, of Cathedral Yard, Exeter. One was a length of needlework rose point, quite equal in design as well as in the quality of workmanship to the original old lace of the sixteenth century. Another was a fine piece of Honiton point proper in a pattern of roses and small floral sprays. A deep flounce with garnitures to match for the bodice is of Flemish design, with scrolls and flowers made of the finest thread, and all thrown up by a connecting groundwork of surpassing lightness, all done with needle and thread. Messrs Atkinson, the well-known poplin weavers, of College Green, Dublin, made a very handsome brocaded poplin of pale green, with a design of Nile lilies and foliage on it in white silk. It was extremely soft, and capable of falling into most graceful draperies.

Messrs Graham, of Mount Street, Grosvenor Square, and the Irish Warehouse, Regent Street, supplied much of the lingerie. Messrs Robinson and Cleaver, of Belfast, supplied some damask napery and household linen, and also some fine pieces of Irish lace. Some fine specimens of Nottingham lace, especially a white lace parasol, with an ivory stick, mounted in gold, was also included in the trousseau, and showed conclusively that in woven laces Nottingham has no rivals. A length of Royal blue silk velvet, woven at Sudbury, in Suffolk, and presented by the ladies of that town, was extremely interesting as a specimen of English manufacture, and vied with the finest products of the looms of Southern France. The Chamber of Commerce of Luton, Bedfordshire, the centre of the straw-plait trade, begged Princess May's acceptance of a cream-straw hat, the very best that could be turned out with all the skill and natural resources at their command.

The Graphic, Royal Wedding Number,
10 July 1893

Maria Carolina, the thirteenth child of the Empress Maria Theresa of Austria and the Emperor Francis I, became Queen of Naples with a trousseau of one hundred dresses, each made in Paris. The size of the trousseau was due to the fact that Maria Carolina only became Ferdinand of Naples' bride because of the deaths of her two sisters, Maria Johanna and Maria Josephine, who had been in turn betrothed to Ferdinand.

While history tells us something of wedding dresses, a number of which can be found in museums and private collections throughout the world, little is known of the clothing of the groom. When breeches and vests were the fashion, men wore special vests embroidered with blue and silver, and there is some historical suggestion that many men married in ceremonial military uniforms. There is little doubt that men made some acknowledgement to their wedding day by wearing a special cravat or stock, or a waistcoat designed for the occasion. The top hat and tails weddings date back to the nineteenth century, the coat belonging even further back to when breeches were worn instead of trousers. As it was with the case of the bride, poorer men would wear their Sunday best, which might be a suit and a clean shirt with a bow tie.

Apart from the preparation of clothes, the engagement permitted time to attend to other matters. The Church requirement for the banns to be called often took place within a few weeks of the betrothal and served to publicize the wedding, thus allowing anyone who objected to the union to make his or her objections known to the priest who was obliged to look into the matter which might delay the nuptials further. Protests to the marriage ranged from claims of consanguinity to statements from rejected lovers. (In parts of the country young couples were advised not to attend the reading of the banns in church as it was thought this would mean that their children would be born deaf and dumb.)

Social customs were slow to change in all aspects of courtship and marriage. From farm workers to the daughters and sons of the aristocracy, an engaged couple seen out together unchaperoned would have been the subject of public ridicule. Queen Victoria was surprised in 1878 when her son Prince Arthur drove alone to Frogmore with his fiancée, Princess Louise of Prussia. She expressed her idea that young people were getting 'very American' in their habits.

It was uncommon for an engagement to be broken. If the woman broke off the engagement she was not ostracized by society in the same way that a man would be; in some way it gave her

IT hardly seems necessary to mention that any public display of affection is ill bred. Love is sacred and beautiful, and it should not be thrown open to the rude comments of strangers. The young couple should conduct themselves with quiet dignity and poise, neither indulging in terms of endearment and caresses, nor purposely ignoring each other so as to create the impression that they are not, after all, so very much in love. There is no reason why their conduct in public after they are engaged should be any different from what it was before.

Lillian Eichler, *A New Book of Etiquette*, 1936

a certain allure. On the other hand a man of the upper classes who broke his word might find himself in social disgrace. If the couple had gone so far as to select a ring the woman might return it, necessary if she broke off the engagement, or she might feel that it was hers to keep.

The rings exchanged and worn at weddings have considerable historical significance. In early ceremonies a ring did not feature in the marriage at all because the contract was a verbal one. Only later, and it is impossible to say exactly when, did rings become an essential part of the marriage. A ring represents a pledge, a sign of a contractual exchange indicating that a deal has been made and that there is an intent for both parties to fulfil their obligations. Amongst people who practised a kind of bride purchase it was a symbol of ownership. It would be too easy to say that betrothal rings, exchanged or given to the bride at the time of the betrothal, and nuptial rings, exchanged at the actual time of the marriage, were replaced in time by engagement rings and wedding rings. Although to a certain extent this was true, the type of rings used in the past did not correspond to the type of rings used today: for example, the popular solitaire or cluster diamond and sapphire engagement rings, and the plain gold wedding band. Early betrothal rings were made of bronze, bone or ivory, later they were made of iron, silver or gold. Although gold is the most popular metal, platignum has been in use for engagement and wedding rings since the late nineteenth century. It was not uncommon for a woman to wear a plain iron ring at home and to put on her gold ring when she went out in public, gold being a precious and costly metal. During the Middle Ages and the Renaissance, betrothal rings were often set with stones, diamonds becoming popular at the end of the fifteenth century. Because of their resistance to fire and steel they remain as popular today.

Early betrothal rings were often known as gemmal or gimmel rings. These were twin rings or double rings (*jumeau* in French means twins), two or more bands which interlaced or locked together to form one ring. Sometimes the ring joined together to form a motif, such as a flower or a pair of clasped hands, and the rings were often engraved on the inner side. Some gimmel rings had three parts – or more – which at the time of the betrothal were broken so that one ring was given to the bride, one to the groom and one to a witness. One medieval ring had four lines inscribed upon its sections reading:

> *Ryches be vnstable*
> *Beuty wyll dekay*
> *But faithfull love wyll ever laste*
> *Tyl deth drive itt away.*

As the betrothal gradually played a less important part in the nuptials, so betrothal rings became less important, and the marriage ring, exchanged or put on the hand of the bride in church, featured more prominently.

The Church was responsible for the change in the nature of the betrothal. Instead of being a contractual arrangement at which gifts – including rings – were exchanged, it had become, by the nineteenth century, an announcement, the beginning of what

Bertha is declared to have a remarkably small finger.

Many couples selected the ring after the engagement had been announced.
Paved with Gold by Mayhew.

we think of today as an engagement and related to a religious ceremony. Under Church doctrine, rings became an essential part of the wedding ceremony. It was impossible to marry without a ring and many priests kept a few plain gold bands to lend to couples who could not afford a ring. Fiction would have us believe that men produce rings, along with the question, when in fact many couples choose the engagement ring together. The selection of the ring is usually carried out fairly swiftly as there exists, still, a feeling that the engagement is somehow less valid without the woman wearing a ring. However, today an engagement ring signifies little unless it is accompanied by a wedding ring – whereas in the past the betrothal ring was viewed as being symbolically important enough in itself. Exactly when the thin gold band of a wedding ring took on such significance is hard to date, but it was likely to be during the sixteenth and seventeenth centuries.

The increasing prominence of the role of the Church in the marriage ceremony resulted in a change as to when the rings were given or exchanged. In the Middle Ages, when the ceremony was often carried out in the porch of the church or outside the church doorway, in order to publicize the wedding according to religious doctrine, rings were exchanged at this time. In later times, as the service moved inside the church, the rings were exchanged at the altar, where they were also blessed by the officiating priest.

ENGAGED COUPLES.

THOUGH man is confessedly the inferior animal, from a social point of view at least, he presents quite as varied aspects when he is in the "engaged" state as woman herself. He behaves in all sorts of ways when brought into that blessed condition, and very often surprises those friends most who thought they knew him best. We feel bound also to declare our belief that analysis of the average engaged man shows his sex to less advantage than it does the other. The number of cold, fickle, or regretable lovers is much greater than of cold, fickle, or regretable beloveds. Men, as a rule, make better bargains than women. We hear people say, "How could she engage herself to that man?" much oftener than "Why did he engage himself to that girl?" And indeed Mother Nature is strong; and it is astonishing how many nice, sensible, delicate girls manage to get themselves betrothed to men who are in every way their inferiors. In the girls' eyes however they are not inferior. At the worst they can offer (and often offer it all the more heartily on account of their inferiority) what every woman claims as her right from her lover—worship. What is it to Maud if Mr. Marmaduke FitzNorman is all that is grand and godlike? He treats her as an ordinary creature of clay: or rather, in spite of his compliments, she feels that she is really nothing more in his eyes. But Tom Smith goes down on his honest knees. What if his clothes are not so well made, and not worn in the same manner?—what if he is sadly deficient in grace, and not unimpeachable in the matter of gloves? To him she is a goddess. All her dainty little feminine ways are as angels' mysteries to him; he is hardly himself in her presence. So her heart is won in spite of thick boots, red hands, and rebellious hair; and well for the world it is that the incense of true devotion should be so sweet in woman's nostrils.

But all lovers, we fear, are not of Thomas Smith's pattern. The truth, the painful truth is, that the heart of the average young man is stuffed full of vain and lofty imaginings concerning his own ability and his own value. He might not admit it even to himself, but his secret belief is that he could win any woman whom he really loved, and made up his mind to win. And he is generally accompanied—in his adolescent years at least, sometimes all through his life—by the image of a wholly impossible angel, who is one day to be his own. This imaginary maiden —"My Queen," as she is called in the song— has all the natural and supernatural virtues as a mere matter of course. An angelic temper,

heroic fortitude, utter unselfishness. radiant beauty, brilliant intellect—well, *there* perhaps something might be remitted, so that there may be no unseemly competition—and above all, a pure and ardent affection for only one person in the world—these are a few of the necessary qualifications of "My Queen." It is only natural for the spirit of man to desire these things, and only natural for one who has some millions of marriageable girls to seek among, to think that somewhere or other he may find them. Furthermore it is not unnatural for a young man who has become engaged to a handsome and nice girl— especially if her social position is a little above his own—to imagine that he has found them. And then, when the wonderful glow which rested upon the world,

"When the happy 'Yes' faltered from her lips,"

has faded a little, and he discovers that he is engaged to a girl not very much more beautiful or very much more adorable than her sisters—a girl with her own little tempers and whims—when he has for the first time seen a frown gather over those eyes that but lately were so tender, the inconstant youth is apt to repent himself. Our readers will probably disbelieve us, but we confess our conviction that an engagement is seldom or never carried through, from the first kiss to the signing of the big

book in the vestry, without some shadow of regret falling on the lover's heart. Perhaps it is because his area of choice is so unconfined by nature; but a man seems to feel the mere fact of being bound in bondage, as a girl does not feel it. Happily however a sensible man does not pay attention to every shadow of regret which falls upon either his heart or his fancy. He recognises the fact that angels are

not to be met with at every corner, and that there never was any human being all that could be desired; and he consoles himself with the reflection that Jane is a good, sensible, and affectionate girl, for whom he has a real affection, and bids adieu to his imaginary "Queen" with what philosophy he can muster.

Many lovers pass through several stages in the course of their engagements; others preserve much the same character throughout. There are two dispositions however which sometimes manifest themselves, and which a girl ought to mark if they are displayed—a jealous temper and a cold impassive behaviour. She may rest assured that in neither respect will her lover's condition improve with marriage. A jealous lover is an intolerable being. Without a husband's rights, he claims a husband's privilege of watching his *fiancée's* conduct,

forbidding her to dance with this man or the other, and makes himself a nuisance generally. A girl may well pause and consider whether she is wise in entrusting her happiness to a man whose love is so selfish and weak as jealous love generally is. As to coldness, a demeanour which will seem frigid to one girl will seem all that is proper to another. Only this disposition too is not one that is mended by marriage. Generally it arises from the fact that the lover has fallen in love with someone else who has refused him; and—not out of pique, but from a longing for companionship—he has proposed to one whom he does not really love. If this be the case, it is better that the engagement should not be continued. Better a little soreness now than a life-long mistake. Better a faithless lover and a solitary fireside, than a loveless marriage and the haunting thought of what might have been.

MILLAMANT: And d'ye hear, I won't be called names after I'm married; positively I won't be called names.

MIRABELL: Names!

MILLAMANT: Ay, as wife, spouse, my dear, joy, jewel, love, sweetheart, and the rest of that nauseous cant, in which men and their wives are so fulsomly familiar – I shall never hear that – Good Mirabell, don't let us be familiar or fond, nor kiss before folks, like my Lady Fadler and Sir Francis: nor go to Hyde Park together the first Sunday in a new chariot, to provoke eyes and whispers: and then never been seen there together again; as if we were proud of one another the first week, and ashamed of one another ever after. Let us never visit together, not go to a play together, but let us be very strange and well bred: let us be as strange as if we had been married a great while; and as well bred as if we were not married at all.

MIRABELL: Item, when you shall be breeding—

MILLAMANT: Ah! name it not.

MIRABELL: Which may be presumed, with a blessing on our endeavours—

MILLAMANT: Odious endeavours!

MIRABELL: I denounce against all strait lacing, squeezing for a shape, 'till you mould my boy's head like a sugar-loaf; and instead of a man-child, make me father to a crooked billet. Lastly, to the dominion of the tea-table I submit. – But with proviso, that you exceed not in your province; but restrain yourself to native and simple tea-table drinks, as tea, chocolate, and coffee. As likewise to genuine and authorised tea-table talk – such as mending of fashions, spoiling reputations, railing at absent friends, and so forth – but that on no account you encroach upon the men's prerogative, and presume to drink healths, or toast fellows; for the prevention of which, I banish all foreign forces, all auxiliaries to the tea-table, as orange-brandy, all aniseed, cinnamon, citron and Barbado's waters, together with ratafia and the most noble spirit of Clary. – But for the cowslip-wine, poppy-water, and all dormitives, those I allow. – These provisos admitted, in other things I may prove a tractable and complying husband.

MILLAMANT: O horrid provisos! filthy strong waters! I toast fellows, odious men! I hate your odious provisos.

MIRABELL: Then we're agreed.

William Congreve, *The Way of the World*

Harrison Fisher's young lady admires her engagement ring in an 1895 issue of the *Illustrated London News.*

And as this round
Is nowhere found
To flaw, or else to sever,
So let our love
As endless prove,
And pure as gold for ever.

Robert Herrick

During the Commonwealth the Puritans tried to abolish the use of rings on the basis that rings were pagan objects. Sometimes, the wife gave the husband not a gold but a silver ring. The two-ring ceremony has itself suffered the whims of fashion. Some people believe that the absence of a wedding ring for the man has more to do with the price of gold than the passing of fashion. It would be impossible to state whether *all* men wore their wedding rings all the time, or if indeed, men wore wedding rings at all. Women most definitely wore them as signs of possession but given the relative freedoms men enjoyed in marriage we can assume that the wearing of a ring by a man was not essential.

There is some doubt as to the origins of the placement of the ring on the fourth finger of the left hand. Many people think that the practice dates back to the Romans who, it is thought, believed that a vein ran from this finger straight to the heart. Other people think that this is simply the most practical finger on which to wear a ring. The left hand is, for most people, the hand used the least and the ring is less likely to be damaged on the fourth finger. The Egyptians, however, wore rings on the third finger of the left hand, while the Gauls and Britons wore wedding rings on their little fingers. There is some evidence to suggest that this practice continued until the Middle Ages. Roman Catholics preferred to use the right hand for betrothal and nuptial rings until the middle of the eighteenth century when it became popular to wear rings on the left hand. Anglo-Saxon children wore their betrothal rings on their right hands until the ceremony when it was placed on the left. The custom of transferring the rings from one finger to the other still exists.

Her Gift (Anon.). The ring – symbol of a contract undertaken for life.

· ˙ On whichever finger or hand rings are worn, they are entirely personal objects. They have been designed in many ways and the inclusion of an inscription or the initials of the couple and the date of the marriage, is the most personal aspect of a wedding ring. Here are some inscriptions taken from seventeenth- and eighteenth-century rings:

> *Love him who gave thee this ring of gold,*
> *'Tis he must kiss thee when thou'rt old.*

> *This circle, though but small about,*
> *The devil, jealousie, shall keep out.*

> *This ring is a token I gave to thee,*
> *That thou no tokens do change for me.*

> *If in thy love thou constant bee,*
> *My heart shall never part from thee.*

> *The eye did find, ye heart did chuse,*
> *The hand doth bind, till death doth loose.*

> *Breake not thy vow to please the eye,*
> *But keepe thy love, so live and dye.*

> *You and I will lovers die.*

> *Thy consent is my content.*

> *Of all the rest I love thee best.*

These two inscriptions are from the nineteenth century:

> *As long as life, Your loving wife.*

> *I did commit no act of folly, when I married my sweet Molly.*

As well as the organization of the rings, there was the wedding feast to be planned. Weddings in rural communities tended to be enormous affairs to which everyone was invited. The cost of such an event was high for whoever was footing the bill. Amongst the early Germanic tribes it was the bridegroom who paid, but it soon became the custom for the father of the bride to host the attendant feast. Occasionally in the past, but more often today, young couples would themselves pay for the weddings; however, poor young people simply could not afford to hold the kind of

Toasts have been part of wedding celebrations for centuries. *The Toast at the Wedding* by Stanhope Alexander Forbes.

big wedding that was expected of them and would wait until their parents were in a financial position to do so.

Big weddings, to which the whole village and surrounding community was invited, were a part of life until the nineteenth century. Everyone would attend, even passing strangers. It was an occasion for fun and frivolity, where old scores were settled, friendships made and renewed, business transacted and further marriages arranged.

One of the more popular ways of holding a wedding was the bride-bush or bride-ale, when the wedding celebration would be held at a tavern and ale sold to the guests in order to pay for the festivities. A large bush was stuck on top of a stake outside the inn so that strangers would be made aware of the bride-ale; they, too, were invited to contribute. 'Penny weddings' were so called as guests contributed to the feast with a collection for the bride and groom, although it was more often a shilling offered by each of the guests to cover the costs.

Perhaps the single most important part of the wedding feast was the wedding cake, as elaborate a confection as the purses of the principal participants could afford. Time was required to make the cake, if it was to be of a fruit mixture laced with liquor to preserve it, while the cake would be iced closer to the day of the wedding. At nineteenth-century Royal weddings several cakes were made and set out on the banqueting tables. There was often a royal wedding cake commissioned by a professional firm of cake makers – many of whom advertised their services in magazines of the day, but the royal kitchen was also called upon to produce a cake. The cake made for the marriage of the Marquis of Lorne and Princess Louise in 1871 was one such cake, produced by Her Majesty's chief confectioner. The *Illustrated London News* described it as 'a perfect triumph of the confectioner's art'. It stood five feet four inches high and had a diameter of two feet six inches. The Royal wedding cake, made by a Messrs Bolland and Son, of Chester, was made in three tiers,

placed on a gold stand, weighing about 2 cwt, and measuring at the base of the lower case 2 ft in diameter, and in height nearly 5 feet. The gold plateau had the Royal arms at four equal distances, with Cupids and flowers. The lower tier was ornamented with blue panels, baskets of flowers, fruit, and love-birds between a scroll leaf, and medallions containing likenesses of the Marquis of Lorne and Princess Louise, with their respective coronets above. The second tier was festooned with the rose, shamrock and thistle. The third tier was entirely of network, with cornucopias and shields, on which were the monograms of the bride and bridegroom. The whole was surmounted by a handsome vase of flowers, with silk banners edged with silver fringe, containing armorial bearings of the Princess and of the Marquis. Each tier of the cake was bordered with trellis-work studded with pearls.

Weddings were occasions for giving and receiving.

— o —

Closer to the day of the wedding a 'bidder', usually an old man, would be sent about the nearby countryside and to all the guests' homes to invite people to the wedding. The invitation was often given in the form of a rhyme. Wealthy people dispatched letters either by sending their servants or using the mail service.

Today most weddings take place in the spring and late summer, times when people hope the weather will be favourable and that most of the guests will be able to attend. In earlier times other considerations played a part in the timing of the wedding. The Romans believed that June was one of the best months in which to marry. Juno was the goddess of

CARMARTHEN, NOV. 20, 1830.

AS we intend to enter the *Matrimonial State*, on *Tuesday*, the 7th Day of *December* next, we are encouraged by our Friends to make a **BIDDING** on the occasion, the same Day, at the Sign of the *Three Salmons, Water Street ;* when and where the favour of your good company is humbly solicited, and whatever donation you may be pleased to bestow on us then, will be received with gratitude, and repaid with punctuality, whenever called for on a similar occasion,

By your humble Servants,

**ROGER HANCOCK,
JANE DAVIES.**

The young Man's Father and Mother (Edward and Jane Hancock,) Brother and Sister (Joseph and Charlotte Hancock,) desire that all Gifts of the above Nature due to them, be returned to the young Man on the said day, and will be thankful together with his Uncle and Aunt (Thomas and Mary Hancock, Three Salmons,) for all favours granted.

Also, the young Woman's Father and Mother (Daniel and Mary Davies,) and Brothers (Thomas, David, and John,) desire that all Gifts of the above Nature due to them, be returned to the young Woman on the above day, and will be thankful for all favours granted.

J. EVANS, PRINTER, CARMARTHEN.

women, who was thought to give a special blessing to marriages. Other popular months have been traditionally January, when ancient fertility rites were carried out, the summer months of July and August, and the harvesting months of October and November. The month of May has long been thought of as an unlucky month in which to marry even though no basis for this superstition exists. To marry on or shortly before the full moon was considered to be a good omen.

The Church attempted to regulate marriages by prohibiting them for almost one third of the year – during Lent, at Rogationtide and from Advent until Christmas. Before the Reformation only thirty-two weeks in the year were granted to religious people in which they could marry without special dispensation. Even after the Reformation, many people continued to adhere to the rules laid down by the Church. When Edward, Prince of Wales, who became Edward VII, was scheduled to marry Princess Alexandra of Denmark in March of 1863 during Lent, Queen Victoria received complaints from the Church on the inappropriate timing of the wedding. She responded that marriage was 'a solemn holy act not to be classed with amusements', and the wedding took place as planned.

The day was important, too. In his Almanac of 1655 Andrew Waterman, a mariner, suggested the following days to marry or contract a wife: 2, 4, 11, 19, 21 January; 1, 3, 10, 19, 21 February; 3, 5, 12, 20, 23 March; 2, 4, 12, 20, 22 April; 2, 4, 12, 20, 23 May; 1, 3, 11, 19, 21 June; 1, 3, 12, 19, 21, 31 July; 2, 11, 18, 20, 30 August; 1, 9, 16, 18, 28 September; 1, 8, 15, 17, 27, 29 October; 5, 11, 13, 22, 25 November; 1, 8, 10, 19, 23, 29 December. Waterman thought that women were supposed to be more loving on these dates.

Fridays were considered unlucky (except in Scotland) as were Saturdays, which seems strange to us as most weddings are held on a Saturday so that all the guests are able to attend. Sunday was a popular day in England.

Monday for wealth
Tuesday for health
Wednesday the best day of all
Thursday for crosses
Friday for losses
Saturday no luck at all

Old English rhyme

Married in Lent,
You'll live to repent.

Old English Saying

There are numerous superstitions associated with the wedding day. It was, for instance, considered unlucky in some parts of England and Wales for married people to attend the wedding ceremony. It was thought unlucky to have an odd number of guests, and it was advisable to invite everyone in order to avoid the curses of those who had not been invited.

One of the most important parts of a wedding was the inclusion of bridesmaids and grooms. The whole idea behind bridesmaids and bridesmen or groomsmen was of sympathetic instinct. It was also a social initiation process by which young men and women, in helping to put the bride and groom to bed (an integral part of the wedding at least until the seventeenth century), could not fail to understand the stress placed on sex and procreation within the context of marriage.

In ancient Britain it was the custom for the bridesmaids to lead the groom to church, and for the bridesmen to fetch the bride from the house of her father and lead her to church.

Even in eighteenth-century Britain it was not unusual for two unmarried men to escort the bride to church while two married men took her home. The symbolism of many of the acts performed by bridesmaids and bridesmen have histories deeply embedded in our pagan past. The 'fetching of the bride'

The Wedding: it was an important wedding custom to include everyone, thus avoiding the curses of uninvited guests.

which, in Wales, for instance, was often carried out on horseback, has its roots in the abduction of women, which was common throughout Europe and not made illegal until the Middle Ages. A male member of the bride's immediate family took the bride up behind him and galloped off into the distance pursued by the men from the groom's family and the groomsmen who finally 'captured' the bride. In other parts of the country, the groomsmen who came to fetch the bride would be forced to engage in a mock battle with her kinsfolk before she was released by them. There is some historic suggestion here that the groomsmen evolved from a military role of protecting the bride from a rival when leading her to church. The best man, it has been suggested, was once the torchbearer, lighting the groom's way in the church.

Bridesmaids were traditionally unmarried girls, while the status of the groomsmen is unknown. The bridesmaids' role was to support the bride morally, if not assist her practically. Pages, trainbearers and ringbearers have been included in wedding services since medieval times. Today's matron of honour was once a brideswoman, an older married woman whose task it was to lead the bride to church and supervise the bridesmaids. Contemporary bridesmaids and groomsmen often provide decorative support rather than hold actual physical responsibilities, which is largely due to the change in manners over the centuries. The bridesmaids no longer deck the wedding bed (the groomsmen now 'decorate' the car in which the couple go away).

The number and age of bridesmaids attending the bride varied in the past as much as it does today. From *Cassells Family Magazine*, 1890.

THE BRIDESMAIDS' DRESSES

OF the ten Royal bridesmaids who attended H.S.H. Princess May of Teck to the altar on the 6th, the Princesses Victoria and Maud of Wales, the Princesses Victoria and Alexandra of Edinburg, and Princess Victoria of Schleswig-Holstein wore very pretty white-satin dresses, the skirts of which were cut long enough to trail about a yard on the ground. Round the bottom of each was a deep chiffon flounce, over which was laid a row of silver and crystal passementerie. The low bodices were cut with rather fantastic basques, which were outlined with the silver passementerie, and finished round the neck with pleatings of chiffon, with two elegant sweeping loops joining in the centre, and the passementerie was laid on this, and carried as a strap over each shoulder. The sleeves consisted of single drooping puffs of chiffon coming down just over the elbow, and each Princess wore a breast-bouquet of pale pink roses. The remaining five bridesmaids, Princess Beatrice of Edinburgh, Princesses Norah and Patricia of Connaught, Princess Eugenie of Battenberg, and Princess Alice – the little daughter of Prince and Princess Louis of Battenberg – wore short frocks of the same white satin, with proportionate chiffon flounces headed with silver passementerie, white satin sashes tied behind, full bodices with chiffon puffings at the top and silver passementerie, and short puff sleeves. They had pink roses on their shoulders. All the satin was of English manufacture, and the silver passementerie was made by cottage workers at Amersham, Penn Street, Winchmore Hill, and the adjacent villages and hamlets of South Bucks. The order for it was given to Messrs. Muddiman, of Tabernacle Street, Finsbury, who have for several years been doing a great deal to cultivate trimming-making as a cottage industry, and also to resuscitate pillow-lace making, with silk and gold and silver threads.

The Graphic, Royal Wedding Number,
10 July 1893

O Bridesmaid, ere the happy knot was tied,
Thine eyes so wept that they could hardly see;
Thy sister smiled and said, 'No tears for me!
A happy bridesmaid makes a happy bride.'
And then, the couple standing side by side,
Love lighted down between them full of glee,
And over his left shoulder laugh'd at thee,
'O happy bridesmaid, make a happy bride.'
And all at once a pleasant truth I learned,
For while the tender service made thee weep,
I loved thee for the tear thou couldst not hide,
And prest thy hand and knew the press returned,
And thought, 'My life is sick of single sleep:
O happy bridesmaid, make a happy bride.'

Alfred, Lord Tennyson, *The Bridesmaid*

———— ♡ ————

Married when the year is new,
He'll be loving, kind and true.
When February birds do mate
You wed nor dread your fate.
If you wed when March winds blow,
Joy and sorrow both you'll know.
Marry in April when you can
Joy for maiden and the man.
Marry in the month of May
And you'll surely rue the day.
Marry when June roses grow
Over land and sea you'll go.
Those who in July do wed
Must labour for their daily bread.
Whoever wed in August be,
Many a change is sure to see.
Marry in September's shine,
Your living will be rich and fine.
If in October you do marry
Love will come, but riches tarry.
If you wed in bleak November
Only joys will come, remember
When December's snows fall fast,
Marry and true love will last.

Anon.

———— ♡ ————

A Wedding Morning by John F. Bacon.

Penny weddings, when the guests contributed to the event, were common in the eighteenth century. From the painting by Sir David Wilkie.

The decking of the bridal bed was most important. Not only were the colours supposed to complement those of the bridal party but the symbolism of each was important for the future welfare of the couple: blue was for constancy; a flesh colour indicated lasciviousness; a straw colour meant plenty; red was for justice. Over the centuries the implications of some colours has changed, as the following examples show: yellow has been thought to symbolize jealousy as well as honour and joy; gold meant avarice to some people and jollity to others; green was for youth, but popinjay-green symbolized wantonness, sea-green inconstancy and willow green being forsaken.

The bridal couple would be required to give the bridesmaids and bridesmen gifts, often in the form of a pair of gloves. The bridegroom often paid for the gloves; sometimes he gave them only to his friends and the bride only to her friends. Sometimes the bride gave gloves to the groomsmen and the bridegroom gloves to the bridesmaids. The custom varied from one part of the country to another.

Each of the bridesmaids – and many of the guests – would carry a nosegay or posy, and the content of these posies was of considerable significance. Some of the old-fashioned flowers included in the posies were lady-smock, prick-madam, gentle-heart and maiden's blush. More familiar flowers were rose, pansy, violet, primrose and orange blossom. Gorse was also included and an old rhyme states that 'when the furze is out of bloom, kissing is out of fashion'. Bay leaf was often found in posies and rosemary, which carries strong historical associations. The plant rosemary was believed to represent remembrance, or to strengthen the memory. It was not only included in nosegays but also used to deck the marriage bed and strewn about the floor of the bridal room. Anne of Cleeves wore a coronet of gold and precious stones set with branches of rosemary at her wedding to Henry VIII.

THE BRIDE'S TRAVELLING COSTUME

THE brides of our English Royal Family always wear white for the wedding journey, and Princess May's was one of the prettiest dresses ever devised, even for such an occasion. It was of cream Irish poplin, and Messrs, Redfern, of New Bond Street, had brought all their well-known taste and skill to bear on it. The skirt was of comfortable walking length, and had a pleating quite round the bottom, the gold embroidery which formed its chief feature being worked on after the seams were done and the length regulated. This was in gold and white silk cord and gold beads, and a succession of three scallops (one over the other) was carried all round, while lines of gold and white cord ascended towards the waist, the spaces between them being dotted with ornaments of gold beads matching those that finished off each end of the scallops. The short jacket-bodice was edged in the same way with three rows of scallops, and lines of silk and gold cord were carried up to meet triple rows of scallops placed the reverse way, even with the tops of the sleeves back and front, the high collar being of folded beaded poplin. The sleeves were coat-shaped and not set in high on the shoulders, and embroidered to match at the wrists. With this was worn a small white poplin mantle to match, edged with one row of scallops round behind, but with two short pointed ends, drawn down in front under a white satin waistband fastened under the left arm with a rosette. There were more gold scallops placed with their points downwards across the bust and shoulders, and a modified Medici collar, high and full behind, but sloped off at the throat, completed one of the most becoming mantles imaginable. The hat had a brim of golden straw, with a crown of rich white silk or poplin, and was trimmed with white roses.

The Graphic, Royal Wedding Number,
10 July 1893

The Coming Event by Jessica Hayllar.

The Big Day

BLEST is the bride that the sun shines on.

Old English Saying

No matter when or where weddings take place, almost every wedding is full of symbolism and tradition from a time of which we have no memory. These rituals stretch back over the centuries, their origins often lost, their significance diluted. It is human nature to take for granted the existence and the tradition of rites and rituals in our lives, largely because it takes generations for them to change. People adhere to tradition at weddings more than at any other time in their lives. Tradition brings with it a sense of security, and an unspoken intimation that if tradition is upheld the wedding will go smoothly and the marriage will be a success. A number of the traditions still in common practice today originated with the ancient Greeks and Romans; many are associated with fertility, sexuality, sympathetic magic; and all are heavy with symbolism.

The inclusion of orange blossom in the bridal wreath or as part of a bouquet dates back to the Saracens, according to some sources. It came to Europe with the returning Crusaders who are believed to have witnessed the custom of a bride wearing a garland – a symbol of maidenhood – of orange blossom on her hair. Orange blossom stands for chastity and purity and, because the orange blossom tree is an evergreen, it also stands for everlasting love.

The horseshoe, which we associate with marriage, has complex meanings. Today it represents good luck. The Greeks and Romans believed that the U-shape was able to protect man from evil. Horseshoes were nailed up on walls in homes and embedded into stone walls. The fact that the horseshoe is nailed with seven iron nails is also significant as they represent the seven gifts of the Holy Spirit. The association with blacksmiths and metallurgy is also important. The water in which a blacksmith washed his hands was considered to contain powerful fertility agents. That the horseshoe is silver is no coincidence: people thought that silver kept witches away.

By all accounts the rhyme 'Something old, Something new, Something borrowed, Something blue' is very old. It is usually interpreted thus. Something old is the garter

The Chapel Royal, Savoy, was crowded on Thursday last, the occasion being the wedding of Mr Alfred Benson, youngest son of the late Mr J. Benson; and Miss Florence Gaultier Dalziel, the youngest daughter of the late Mr Davidson Dalziel. The service was fully choral. Besides the six bridesmaids – whose dresses, and that of the bride, were described in *The Lady* last week – there were two little girls (the Misses Maple) in white India muslin frocks and big Kate Greenaway daffodil-yellow sashes. The grown-up bridesmaids were all very tall. Mrs Dalziel was tastefully dressed in ruby velvet, the front of her dress being beaded with tiny loops of ruby beads. Among the more noticeable dresses was that of one of the guests, who was tall and handsome. She wore golden-brown velvet, and carried a large bunch of tea roses, arranged with their own leaves, and tied with green ribbon. Another dress was of mouse-grey velvet, and its wearer carried a large bunch of pale pink tulips. The Rev. Henry White performed the wedding ceremony, the bride being given away by her uncle, Mr George Dalziel. Mr Arthur Benson, the bridegroom's brother, was best man. After the marriage a large party of relatives and friends assembled at Carlyle House, on the Chelsea Embankment – the residence of the bride's brother-in-law and sister, Mr and Mrs F. E. Colman – where the wedding breakfast was given. The honeymoon is being spent in Paris.

The Lady, 19 March 1885

of a happily married woman. Something new is usually the wedding dress. Something borrowed can be a coin (it was once a piece of gold which represented the sun) but it could be any of the wedding items – even a pair of shoes. Some people believe that the bridegroom should supply the coin which, if the bride wears it in her shoe during the ceremony, will ensure a happy marriage. Something blue was associated with the idea of protection and represents the moon, the traditional protector of women. To the Ancient Egyptians blue was the colour of heaven.

The kiss is a way of sealing a pledge. There is an old custom which states that the bride must cry at the end of the ceremony or there will be tears during the marriage. In medieval times brides were supposed to cry or their virtue was suspected.

For centuries brides have worn a wedding veil. It was designed to keep the 'evil eye' from seeing the bride, to deter the malevolent glance from a jealous person which, it was believed, could ruin a potentially happy marriage. The early wedding veil originated as a canopy under which the bridal party travelled to meet the bridegroom. Anglo-Saxons married under a veil held at each corner by a man. When the veil was raised it was symbolic of the bride being free of parental control and this still holds true today. The veil was also used symbolically to incorporate children of previous marriages.

A bride's bouquet, which often includes orange blossom, is tied with many knots. The knots are lover's knots, symbols of hope, love and good fortune. When the bride throws her bouquet after the ceremony, whoever catches it is thought to be the next person to marry. Rice is a symbol of fertility which is why it was thrown at the couple

– and still is today, although few people understand the reason why. Rice has been replaced mostly today with paper confetti. The almond was a symbol of undying love and youth, hence its appearance at weddings in a sugared form and given as gifts, or favours, to young members of the bridal party. (The Victorians associated the almond with stupidity, since the almond tree blossomed so early in spring.)

We know little about weddings prior to the seventeenth century and what we do know was often subject to editing by writers who did not approve of wedding-day rites, finding suggestions of paganism in much of the day's activities, and deploring the size of the wedding and the costs involved and the emphasis on the bedding of the bride and groom.

One of the traditions that has changed little over the centuries is the site of the wedding. Today many brides still return home to their natal parish, or at least to the home of their parents, from which the bridal party leaves and to which it often returns for the wedding reception. For as long as the parents of the bride have been paying for the wedding, their home has been the backdrop to the celebrations. From here, for weddings amongst poor people, the bride was 'fetched', sometimes, in the case of country weddings, meeting the groom and his party *en route* to the church.

Hear the mellow wedding bells, –
Golden bells!
What a world of happiness their harmony foretells!
Through the balmy air of night
How they ring out their delight!
From the molten golden notes,
What a liquid ditty floats
To the turtle-dove that listens, while she gloats
On the moon!
Oh, from out the sounding cells,
What a gush of euphony voluminously wells!
How it swells!
How it dwells
On the Future! How it tells
Of the rapture that impels
To the swinging and the ringing
Of the bells, bells, bells,
Of the bells, bells, bells, bells,
Bells, bells, bells, –
To the rhyming and the chiming of the bells!

Edgar Allan Poe, *The Bells*

Engraving after Richard Westall, 1800.

SHE sang as she dressed with the shrill sweetness of a robin. She had never seen such garments; she hardly knew how to put some of them on. She brushed her hair till it shone like a tiger-lily, and piled it on her small head in great plaits. When her white muslin frock was on, she drew a long breath, seeing herself in bits in the small glass. . . .

Not many brides think so little of themselves, so much of small pensioners, as Hazel did this morning. Breakfast was a sociable meal, for Abel made several remarks. Now and then he looked at Hazel and said, 'Laws!' Hazel laughed gleefully. When she stood by the gate watching for the neighbour's cart that was to take them, she looked as full of white budding promise as the may-tree above her.

She did not think very much about Edward, except as a protecting presence. Reddin's face, full of strong, mysterious misery; the feel of Reddin's arm as they danced; his hand, hot and muscular, on hers – these claimed her thoughts. She fought them down, conscious that they were not suitable in Edward's bride.

At last the cart appeared, coming up the hill with the peculiar lurching deportment of market carts. The pony had a bunch of marigolds on each ear, and there was lilac on the whip. They packed the animals in – the cat giving ventriloquial mews from her basket, the rabbit in its hutch, the bird in its wooden cage, and Foxy sitting up in front of Hazel. The harp completed the load. They drove off amid the cheers of the next-door children, and took their leisurely way through the resinous fragrance of larch-woods.

The cream-coloured pony was lame, which gave the cart a peculiar roll, and she was tormented with hunger for the marigolds, which hung down near her nose and caused her to get her head into strange contortions in the effort to reach them. The wind sighed in the tall larches, and once again, as on the day of the concert, they bent attentive heads towards Hazel. In the glades the wide-spread hyacinths would soon be paling towards their euthanasia, knowing the art of dying as well as that of living, fortunate, as few sentient creatures are, in keeping their dignity in death.

When they drove through the quarry, where deep shadows lay, Hazel shivered suddenly.

'Somebody walking over your grave,' said Abel.

'Oh, dunna say that! It be unlucky on my wedding-day,' she cried. As they climbed the hill she leaned forward, as if straining upwards out of some deep horror.

When their extraordinary turn-out drew up at the gate, Abel boisterously flourishing his lilac-laden whip and shouting elaborate but incomprehensible witticisms, Edward came hastily from the house. His eyes rested on Hazel, and were so vivid, so brimful of tenderness, that Abel remained with a joke half expounded.

'My Hazel,' Edward said, standing by the cart and looking up, 'welcome home, and God bless you!'

'You canna say fairer nor that,' remarked Abel. 'Inna our 'Azel peart? Dressed up summat cruel inna she?'

Edward took no notice. He was looking at Hazel, searching hungrily for a hint of the same overwhelming passion that he felt. But he only found childlike joy, gratitude, affection, and a faint shadow for which he could not account, and from which he began to hope many things.

If in that silent room upstairs he had come to the opposite decision; if he had that very day told Hazel what his love meant, by the irony of things she would have loved him and spent on him the hidden passion of her nature.

But he had chosen the unselfish course.

'Well,' he said in a business-like tone, 'suppose we unpack the little creatures and Hazel first?'

Mrs Marston appeared.

'Oh, are you going to a show, Mr Woodus?' she asked Abel. 'It would have been so nice and pleasant if you would have played your instrument.'

'Yes, mum. That's what I've acome for. I inna going to no show. I've come to the wedding to get my belly-full.'

Mrs Marston, very much flustered, asked what the animals were for.

'I think, mother, they're for you.' Edward smiled.

She surveyed Foxy, full of vitality after the drive; the bird, moping and rough; the rabbit, with one ear inside out, looking far from respectable. She heard the ventriloquistic mews.

'I don't want them, dear,' she said with great decision.

'It's a bit of a cats' 'ome you're starting, mum,' said Abel.

Mrs Marston found no words for her emotions.

But while Edward and Abel bestowed the various animals, she said to Martha:

'Weddings are not what they were, Martha.'

'Bride to groom,' said Martha, who always read the local weddings: 'a one-eyed cat; a foolish rabbit as'd be better in a pie; an ill-contrived bird; and a filthy smelly fox!'

Mrs Marston relaxed her dignity so far as to laugh softly. She decided to give Martha a rise next year.

From Mary Webb, *Gone to Earth*

JUST as the wedding guests were entering one of the uptown churches a few days since, a carriage drove up containing the wife and three children of the bridegroom. Of course the young lady didn't care to become the bride in the face of this circumstance. There was quite a discussion, a little crying, an attempt to hush the matter up and the guests departed.

The Times Picayune, New Orleans

WEDDING GIFTS

Wedding gifts were brought to the wedding itself, if they had not been received beforehand, just as they are today, and the bride and groom handed out their gifts to the groomsmen and bridesmaids either immediately prior to the wedding ceremony or at the wedding feast itself. This custom is impossible to date; like many traditions it has been handed down over the centuries and its origins were never documented. Wedding gifts used to be displayed at the reception far more than they are today. Gifts at royal weddings, in particular, attracted a great deal of interest from the general public. The *Illustrated London News* devoted several pages to the gifts given to the Duke and Duchess of York on their wedding in April 1923. There follows a list of some of the items the couple received:

Mustard and pepper pots (The Civil Service Sports Council)
A gilt clock (The Princess Royal)
A porcelain lamp (The King and Queen of Denmark)
An antique Parliament clock of about 1797 (Coutt's Bank)
One of a pair of vases (The Prince Regent of Japan)
Gold fruit knives (The King and Queen and Crown Prince of Norway)
Table silver (Twelve City Companies)
Silver candelabra (The King and Queen, part of the King's gift to his son, and
    the Queen's gift to him, consisting of silver baskets and canteens of cutlery)
Antique silver tray, 30 inches long and weighing 271 oz by Paul Horr – 1813
    (The United Grand Lodge of England)
A gold cigarette case (The King and Queen of Spain)
A gold cigarette case (King Alexander of Serbia)
A silver vase (The Mayor, Alderman and Councillors of the City of Westminster)
A green tray with diamond-set arrow (The Infanta Beatrice and Alfonso of Spain)
Seventeenth-century Chinese lacquer jewel casket on Queen Anne stand carved and
    gilt (Lord and Lady Waring)
A pair of mahogany tallboys of the Chippendale period (Sir Philip Sassoon)
An old Chinese lacquer cabinet on antique English stand of carved gilt wood
    (Viscount Leverhulme)
An inlaid cabinet (Duke and Duchess of Portland).

The object of wedding gifts is, as it always was, to furnish the couple with as much as possible in the way of items for the household so that they should have to purchase little, if nothing. Personal gifts to the bride and groom independently were given by close relatives, often in the form of jewellery, and a marriage was seen by parents as an appropriate occasion to settle jewellery and valuables upon their children.

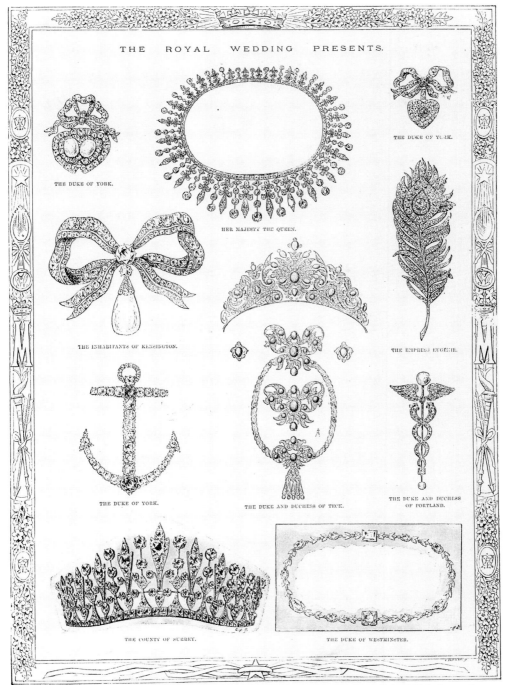

Wedding gifts for the Duke and Duchess of York, who married in July 1893, from the *Illustrated London News*.

ALTHOUGH they had met only once, in 1911, Her Royal Highness Princess Viktoria Luise of Prussia and His Royal Highness Prince Ernst August of Hanover were so much in love that they wanted to marry each other. The political, dynastic and constitutional problems to such a union would have presented an insurmountable obstacle just thirty years earlier, but in the dawn of a new century the parties managed to work out a compromise. Viktoria Luise was from the Hohenzollern family, the daughter of Wilhelm II, King of Prussia and the German Kaiser. Ernst August was a Guelph, the only son of the Duke of Cumberland, Duke of Brunswick and Luneberg, and heir to the Hanovarian throne.

In order to facilitate the match, the Duke of Cumberland renounced the throne of the Duchy of Brunswick and Luneberg in favour of Ernst August, and the young prince took the oath of the Order of the Black Eagle, which bound him to the King of Prussia. He was no longer a Bavarian officer. The Kaiser also bestowed the Order of the Black Eagle on the Duke of Cumberland, and the Order of Queen Luise on the Duchess of Cumberland. But for the supporters and political factions of the houses of Hohenzollern and Guelph this was not enough. The Prussians demanded that Ernst August renounce his rights to the Hanoverian throne, while the Guelphs wanted the accession to the Brunswick throne to represent the start of a Guelph restoration. The families ignored the political badgering and the engagement was announced in February of 1912.

The wedding was scheduled for 24 May and a few days before the wedding guests began to arrive, the most important being the Czar of Russia, Nicholas II, and King George V of England and his wife Queen Mary. (Princess Viktoria Luise was the granddaughter of Princess Victoria, the Princess Royal, Queen Victoria's eldest daughter, and Ernst August was related to George III.) The wedding gifts were set out on view and they included a diadem and pearl necklace from the Kaiser; a diamond tiara from the Kaiserin; and a complete jewellery outfit from the bridegroom. Other gifts of jewellery came from Alexandra, the English Queen Mother, who gave Viktoria Luise an emerald brooch; from the Czar came an aquamarine and diamond necklace; from Brunswick came a diadem which had been worn by the Empress Josephine; and from King George and Queen Mary came a diamond brooch and a gold goblet. Other heads of state sent antiques: the gift of Queen Wilhelmina of Holland was an antique pendulum clock, and the Italian King and Queen sent antique silver vessels. In her memoirs, the Princess recalled that the gifts were numerous enough to require several furniture vans to move them.

On 24 May, Princess Viktoria Luise and Prince Ernst August were married, first in a civil ceremony, followed by a religious ceremony in the chapel at the New Palace. The bridal procession, led by the Corps of Pages, was composed of the bride and groom, the immediate bridal family, all the visiting heads of states and a retinue of Princes, Princesses, Dukes and Duchesses. At the chapel the procession joined other invited guests: the Chancellor, the

Ministers of State, members of the Federal Council and the Field Marshals.

Bright sunlight filtered through the chapel cupola as Ernst August and I stepped up to the altar which my mother and Crown Princess Cecilie, my sister-in-law, had decorated with roses, carnations and wreaths. Pastor Dryander had delivered his sermon, earnest and worthy words which warned me about the seriousness of life.

After that came the actual marriage ceremony. Ernst August's 'yes' rang out so loudly and clearly that I had to follow suit and when we joined hands in front of the altar he clasped mine very firmly, insisting that his thumbs were on top of mine. You see, there's an old folk-tale which says that if the husband does not have his thumbs above those of his bride at the wedding ceremony then he will have no say during his marriage. Pastor Dryander looked slightly shocked at this little demonstration, but Ernst August and I just smiled at each other.

As soon as the vows and rings had been exchanged, the battery of the 1st Guards Field Artillery Regiment fired a thirty-six-gun salute, the chapel bells rang out in loud peals, and the wedding party made its way to the White Hall again, where we stood under the canopy of the Throne and received congratulations from the guests filing past, as the orchestra played the 'Wedding March' from *Midsummer Night's*

Dream. My husband and I had my father standing to our right together with my mother-in-law, Queen Mary and the Czar, and on our left my mother, my father-in-law, Crown Princess Cecilie and King George V.

In the nearly eighty years that have passed since this wedding, Europe has changed beyond recognition. The Czar was to live only a few more years, two world wars were to separate England and Germany so that it was over fifty years before another English head of state set foot on German soil. Never again would Berliners, or in fact, any country, see such a large assembly of monarchs at one wedding.

In some parts of Britain the bride and groom were led in a musical procession to the church gate. In Scotland the bagpipes and musketry marched out ahead of the bride to meet the groom's party. Obviously, the superstition that the bride and groom should not see each other on the day of the wedding until they met in church did not exist at this time. Today the bride has a greater choice in the mode of transport she employs to get her to the church. Before the invention of the car horses and carriages were the only means of transport and the type used depended upon the wealth of the bride's family. If no vehicle was available, brides travelled on horseback or on foot.

The bride in all her finery, the groom dressed up in his best clothes, their pages, attendants, family, relatives and friends gathered initially at the church door for the wedding ceremony; only later did the bridal party move inside. It has been suggested by many historians that weddings were once noisy affairs, accompanied by much shouting and teasing from the guests who, having taken a day off, and looking forward to an afternoon and evening of dancing, drinking, eating and revelry, were difficult for the priest to control. Many of the guests would otherwise never appear in church and their disrespect for the church shocked the priests. Weddings amongst poor people appear to have been extremely bawdy affairs – the custom of tearing off the garters of the bride and carrying them about the church was thought to be disgraceful by the village élite.

Midday – The Wedding Party
by Albert Fitch Bellows.

¶ Then shall the Minister say,

Who giveth this Woman to be
married to this Man?

¶ Then shall they give
their troth to each other
in this manner, The Minister, receiving
the Woman at her Father's
hands, shall cause the
Man with his right hand
to take the Woman by her
right hand, and to say
after him as followeth,

HENRY · GEORGE · CHARLES
take thee VICTORIA ·
ALEXANDRA · ALICE · MARY
to my wedded wife, to have
and to hold from this day
forward, for better for worse,
for richer for poorer, in
sickness and in health, to
love and to cherish,
till death us do part,

11.

Princess Mary received from the Queen an illuminated marriage service on her wedding in March 1922.

MEG looked very like a rose herself; for all that was best and sweetest in heart and soul seemed to bloom into her face that day, making it fair and tender, with a charm more beautiful than beauty. Neither silk, lace, nor orange-flowers would she have. 'I don't want to look strange or fixed up to-day,' she said. 'I don't want a fashionable wedding, but only those about me whom I love, and to them I wish to look and be my familiar self.'

So she made her wedding gown herself, sewing into it the tender hopes and innocent romances of a girlish heart. Her sisters braided up her pretty hair, and the only ornaments she wore were the lilies of the valley which 'her John' liked best of all the flowers that grew.

'You *do* look just like our own dear Meg, only so very sweet and lovely that I should hug you if it wouldn't crumple your dress,' cried Amy, surveying her with delight, when all was done.

'Then I am satisfied. But please hug and kiss me, every one, and don't mind my dress; I want a great many crumples of this sort put into it to-day'; and Meg opened her arms to her sisters, who clung about her with April faces for a minute, feeling that the new love had not changed the old.

Louisa M. Alcott, *Good Wives*

In addition, the bridal pair were showered with nuts and shells, and even sods, inside the church. Weddings were seen as occasions of fun, a community activity that bonded the guests and underlined the importance of the day to the bridal couple. Puritans felt that the atmosphere of frivolity undermined the seriousness of the event, while others believed that the antics of the assembled company served to mask the emotion, the nervous anticipation and excitement that was felt by even the most cynical of wedding guests.

The custom of the priest kissing the bride, after the ceremony had taken place, was a signal for the members of the congregation to push and shove to get close enough to the bride to plant kisses on her themselves. This custom, along with others that the Church found increasingly undignified and inappropriate for the priests to participate in, was gradually dropped in the seventeenth and eighteenth centuries.

There existed in many parts of Britain a custom by which children blocked the way of the bridal pair to their wedding feast until a forfeit or fine had been paid. In Wales children who had made a garland of evergreens and flowers held it in front of the couple outside the church and demanded money before they would allow the bride and groom to pass. In the north of England people in the street begged the bride and groom for money, or children requested coins with which to buy toys. If the groom was sensible he carried loose change with him, or his best man would be obliged to dig into his own pockets. There were horseback races to the house of the bride, or races on foot, the winner claiming the right to remove the bride's garter.

If the bride's garters had not been torn from her after the wedding ceremony in church, they would be removed at the wedding feast. Although there is evidence of the taking of the garter all over Britain the custom seems to have been played out to a greater or lesser extent in different parts of the country. In some places the garters of both bride and groom were taken, but it was most usual for the bride's skirts to be

Signing the Register by James Charles. An important part of the ceremony.

Nineteenth-century medieval fantasy – the groom is called away
immediately after his wedding ceremony. *To Arms!*
by Edmund Blair Leighton.

lifted and the garter snatched by the groomsmen. Some brides carried extra garters to fling to everyone. In parts of Scotland brides had garters, or bits of ribbon sewn to their wedding dresses, so that there would be plenty to pass amongst everyone. Where there was only one garter it was often cut up into small pieces and given out to the wedding guests, who pinned these bits of ribbon to their clothes. It is from here that historians suggest that the custom of bridal guests wearing coloured ribbons emerged.

Once the Church discouraged the taking of the garter inside the chapel itself, which it had begun to do increasingly from the sixteenth century, the party had to wait until the wedding feast, or until the couple were bedded. By the eighteenth century social attitudes amongst the wealthy found that bawdy activities of garter-taking and the bedding of the bride and groom to be distasteful enough to prevent them from attending the wedding celebrations. They would send gifts and stay at home.

Receptions were held at home: *The Return from Church* (Anon.).

WENT to Emily Grimston's marriage at Gorhambury on my way to Hatfield. They were married in the house by the Dean of Carlisle, about thirty people present and a breakfast to the county afterwards. I was heartily glad when it was over – nothing is so melancholy as a wedding when one considers the many chances for its turning out ill; and how often both parties may wish in vain those awful and irrevocable words then said, *unsaid*.

Carola Oman, *The Gascoyne Heiress, The Life and Diaries of Frances Mary Gascoyne-Cecil 1802–39*

Ten mile wood an' bramble, and three mile field an' dew,
In the cold smile of morning, I walked, to marry you;
No horse had I but my wishes – no pilot but a star;
But my boyish heart it fancied it heard you from afar.

So through the woods I hurried, an' through the grass an' dew,
An little I thought o' tiring, the whole of my journey through;
Things ne'er before nor after do soa man rejoice,
As on the day he marries the woman of his choice!

And then our country wedding – brimful o' grief an' glee,
With every one a-pettin' an' jokin' you an' me;
The good cheer went and came, wife, as it sometimes has done
When clouds have chased each other across the summer sun.

There was your good old father dressed up in weddin' shape,
With all the homespun finery that he could rake an' scrape;
And your dear-hearted mother, the sunlight of whose smile
Shone through the showers of tear-drops that stormed her face the while;

Also your sisters an' brothers who hardly seemed to know
How they could scare up courage to let their sister go;
An' cousins an' school-house comrades, dressed up in meetin' trim,
With one of them a-sulkin' because it wasn't him;

An' there was the good old parson, his neck all dressed in white,
A bunch o' texts in his left eye, a hymn-book in his right;
And the parson's virgin daughter, plain an' severely pure,
Who hoped we should be happy, but wasn't exactly sure;

And there was the victuals, seasoned with kind regards an' love,
And holly-wreaths with the breastpins of rubies, up above;
An' there was my heart a-wonderin' as how such things could be,
And there was all the world before us, and there was you and me.

Will Carleton, *The Golden Wedding*

THE marriage of Lord Anglesey and Lady Marjorie Manners may be said to have marked the close of the season for 1912, and a most brilliant wind-up did this important event prove. Lady Anglesey has always on account of her good looks, her vivacity, and her talents been a great favourite of the public in general and the photographic press in particular, and thousands turned up to see her married and to enjoy the excitement of seeing the many celebrities who attended the ceremony. After the bride and bridegroom, who made a splendid pair, those who attracted the greatest amount of admiration were the little pages and trainbearers, who looked perfectly sweet and behaved accordingly.

The Tatler, 14 August 1912

Jessica Hayllar's sumptuous *Wedding Reception* shows the formality of society weddings in the nineteenth century.

The *Illustrated London News* of 1858 gave its opinion of the fashionable wedding.

The Gascoyne Heiress was married from the house in which she had been born on Friday, 2 February 1821. John Bull commented unctuously:

MARRIAGE IN THE HIGH LIFE

YESTERDAY evening, at eight o'clock, Lord Viscount Cranborne, the only son of the Marquess of Salisbury, led to the Hymeneal altar the accomplished daughter of Mr Bamber Gascoyne, in the presence of the Duke of Wellington, Marquess and Marchioness of Salisbury, Countess of Westmeath, Marchioness Dowager of Downshire, the Ladies Hill, Lord Arthur Hill, General and the two Misses Gascoyne, Mr and Mrs Evelyn, Mrs and Miss Stewart and the Earl of Clarendon.

The ceremony was performed in the Great Saloon of Mr Gascoyne's house by the Hon. and Rev. Gerald Wellesley. The Duke of Wellington gave the Lady away. The bridesmaids were the Misses Gascoyne, her cousins. The bride was habited in a superb dress of Valenciennes lace and looked most lovely. After the ceremony the happy pair left town for Mr Daniel Giles's beautiful seat called Youngsbury in Hertfordshire, there to pass the honeymoon.

*

The *County Chronicle* with local patriotism added that the Rector of Hatfield, the Rev Mr Faithfull, had assisted Dr Wellesley, that both Lord Cranborne's married sisters had been present, and that the splendid emblazoned chariot in which the bride and bridegroom had left Great Stanhope Street had been launched specially for the occasion.

The principal officiating clergyman was the youngest brother of the Duke of Wellington. The Ladies Hill were nieces of the 1st Marchioness of Salisbury, and Lord Arthur, who had been an aide-de-camp to his cousin, the Duke, at Waterloo, was their brother. There were actually three Gascoyne sisters as well as three sons, but, according to John Leigh, Miss Charlotte Gascoyne was already betrothed.

The signatures to the marriage settlement, dated February 2nd, were Salisbury, E. M. Salisbury, Cranborne, Bamber Gascoyne, F. M. Gascoyne, Clarendon, Gerald Wellesley, Wellington and Dacre. Nothing need be deduced from *John Bull*'s failure to note the bride's grandmother, Mrs Chase Price, as one of those present. She was in cheerful correspondence six weeks later.

To ask the Duke of Wellington to give away the bride was not unprecedented. In 1819 he had given away the Vane-Tempest heiress on her marriage to the widower Lord Stewart, afterwards 3rd Marquess of Londonderry. But in that case the bride had no father and the bridegroom had served under the Duke in the Peninsula as Adjutant-General.

Carola Oman, *The Gascoyne Heiress, The Life and Diaries of Frances Mary Gascoyne-Cecil 1802–39*

Medieval marriage feasts lasted for hours with many different courses.

Other than the ceremony itself, the most important part of the wedding was the feast afterwards. Once the engagement had been announced people began to cook and store food for the wedding feast. A cake was baked, meats cured and salted, and all kinds of treats stored and hidden until the day of the wedding. The wealthy had an army of servants to prepare and serve the food, but the less well-off helped each other out, the men setting up tables and the women laying out the food. Neighbours and friends often supplied additional food for the table. All the guests would expect the largest display of food and drink that the parents of the bride could afford and the parents would provide it knowing that, in many cases, they would be reimbursed by donations from the guests. The centerpiece of the spread was the wedding cake. At the wedding feast the wedding cake was crumbled in pieces over the heads of the couple to bring good luck. An old custom has the bride putting a piece of the wedding cake under her marriage bed as a symbol of fidelity, and yet another custom has the bride keeping one tier of her wedding cake to be eaten at the christening of her first child. One custom that seems to have survived is that of the distribution of the wedding cake. In the past a small piece was often passed through the wedding ring of the bride, and crumbs were showered on the heads of both bride and groom.

Simple or lavish, wedding days captured Victorian imaginations. *A Sailor's Wedding* by Charles Green.

A WEDDYNGE BREAKFASTE
Monday, October 22, 1849

UP, and to Church together with my Wife, to see PALL HARLEY married this Morning to DICK BAKER; on both Sides mighty genteel People, and their Guests, all except ourselves, such as they do call Carriage-Company. PALL, in a Dress of White Satin, and Orange Flowers in her Hair, very pretty and demure, and DICK, wearing a Sky-Blue Coat, Crimson Velvet Waistcoat, Yellow Moleskin Trowsers, and Japanned Boots: with Lavender Kid Gloves, and a Carbuncle in his Shirt-Front, a great Buck. DICK and every Man of us with great White Favours at our Breasts, mighty conspicuous and, methought, absurd, the Things serving neither for Use nor Ornament. But to see how grand were old fat MR HARLEY and MR BAKER, and how more grand were their fat Wives, and how fine and serious they looked and how high they carried their Noses! And when the Ring was put on PALL's Finger (DICK first having fumbled for it in the wrong Pocket), her Mother did weep, and, falling for support on MR HARLEY, nigh overthrew him. But the pretty modest Bridesmaids did most of all take me; which my Wife observing, I saw, did trouble her. The Ceremony over, and the Fees paid, and the Bride kissed by some of the old Gentlemen, we to old HARLEY's to Breakfast, where what WIGGYNS do call a Grand Spread, very fine both for Show and Meats, every Dish ornamented with Flowers.

Mr Pips His Diary

We do not know whether weddings were loud affairs prior to the sixteenth century, or whether they had slowly become enormous noisy celebrations. In either case the raucous weddings of the sixteenth and seventeenth centuries were to change by the following century. As people tried to emanate the class above them they copied the wealthy and aristocratic forms of marriage which were conducted in a more decorous fashion, the bawdy songs contained until after the priest had left the feast. Wealthy people in seventeenth-century France avoided the bedding custom by holding the marriage at two or three o'clock in the morning, the bride and groom then hosting a supper until dawn.

The bedding of the bride and groom took place after the food had been consumed, the toasts made, the jokes told, the singing over, and the games finished. The couple were escorted to bed, to the house of the groom, if it was near by, or to a house which had been loaned to them. Here they were undressed by their own groomsmen or bridesmaids, put into their nightclothes and placed into the bed which the priest might have been persuaded to bless. (In Austria the bride was stripped naked, which was symbolic of ridding her of all her possessions before the marriage.) The bed would have been dressed up with ribbons and herbs strewn about the floor. Many of the company assembled to see the couple in bed and it was at this point that the bride was persuaded to part with her stocking.

Stocking-throwing, like the taking of the garter, was an integral part of wedding ceremonies until the seventeenth, and even the eighteenth, centuries. Of course the manner in which the stocking was thrown varied from region to region, but one of the most popular methods seems to have been for the bride to sit up backwards in bed and throw the stocking over her shoulder to the assembled company who scrambled to grab it. The lucky recipient was thought to be the next person to marry, and in this way the stocking-throwing resembles the bouquet-tossing that takes place just before the bride leaves on her honeymoon today. And while garters are still worn today, if they are removed at all, it is carried out in a decorous fashion by the best man. In the nineteenth century the bride threw her slipper, usually before she left the wedding reception – as it had begun to be known – for her honeymoon. Today's brides throw their bouquets, but a custom concerning shoes still prevails.

The old shoes that, in England, are tied to the rear of the car in which the couple leave the wedding party for their honeymoon are symbolic on several counts. Shoes are, in an ancient sense, connected to the transfer of property, a shoe being removed and exchanged to confirm a transaction. They were also symbolic of the transfer of authority between one man and another, in the case of marriage between parent or guardian and husband. It has been suggested that shoes are supposed to represent the female organs, thus associating with fertility. It was an old custom amongst the Greeks, Romans and then the German peoples for the bride to remove her shoe and throw it in the direction of the guests. Whoever caught this symbol of good luck was believed to be the next person to marry.

A posset was often drunk in the bridal chamber, first by the bride and groom and then by the guests who crowded into the room. When the couple were finally left

Blessing the nuptial bed was a custom that fell out of favour during the eighteenth century.
Bénédiction du Lit Nuptial.

alone they might find that their sheets had been sewn together – a prank carried out by the bridesmaids. George III and his queen were the first royal couple not to have to undergo the custom of bedding, stocking-throwing and posset-drinking.

In time the middle and lower classes began copying the wealthier classes in all aspects of the wedding, dispensing with the games, the kissing and the garter-taking, stocking-throwing and jesting. Weddings became more private affairs, with carefully drawn lists of invited guests. They also became more respectable. A solemn marriage service, accompanied by appropriate music (we do not know whether music was incorporated in earlier church ceremonies) was followed by a reception in a marquee or hotel rooms rented for the occasion. Most of the popular wedding marches or musical pieces played at weddings originated in the late nineteenth and early twentieth centuries. A wedding breakfast or supper took the place of an all-day, all-night feast and afterwards the couple left alone for a honeymoon on the English coast or Europe if it could be afforded.

The fashion of going away on a holiday immediately after the wedding did not catch hold until the eighteenth century; and then, it is believed, it coincided with the demise of the bedding of the bridal couple. As weddings were such public events, it was not considered important for the couple to spend time alone together immediately after the nuptials. The aristocratic couple would travel to the home or seat of the husband where they would begin married life, receiving visitors and introducing the bride to her new neighbours. Wealthy townspeople might stay at home to greet visiting guests, but for those who worked the day after their wedding was just like any other.

The honeymoon, which we have come to think of as being a time when couples spend several weeks alone together, is a relatively late marriage custom. Honeymoons were first taken by the upper classes, according to John R. Gillis in his book *For Better, For Worse*, from the 'desire to emphasize conjugality'. As mentioned earlier the honeymoon – although it wasn't known by this name at the time – evolved from the period of negotiation after the abduction of the bride when the husband and father of the bride agreed on the terms of the marriage. The time allowed angry feelings to subside and for everyone involved to get used to a new situation. The bride might remain in relative seclusion with her new husband until she could be sure that her family would not seek revenge. Perhaps from this time, too, comes the suggestion that the word 'honeymoon' comes from a mead – made from honey – which was drunk every night for the first month of the marriage. There have been other more romantic interpretations of the word honeymoon.

Honeymoons as we think of them began to be popular during the late eighteenth century when people travelled more and it became the custom, amongst those who could afford it, to travel with their new wives. What may seem most curious to us now is that the couple did not travel alone but with their family and friends. One of the most likely reasons for this was that on many occasions the couple barely knew each other and would find each other's company a great strain. When making his honeymoon plans in 1848 John Ruskin expected his parents to join him and his wife, Effie Grey, in the Alps, and this practice was only just beginning to be considered unusual. It wasn't until the late nineteenth century that the practice of bringing family and friends along became less popular – which suggests that as couples married for love, they no longer felt the necessity for anyone else's company but each other's.

Popular honeymoon destinations have changed somewhat. In England in the nineteenth century, Pegwell Bay was a great favourite, with other English seaside resorts becoming increasingly popular. The novelist Elinor Glynn, sister of the dress

Earl of Kildare to Countess of Kildare
Rostellan, 30 June 1752

THE house is very large and odd. I have a very good bedchamber, and a large good new bed, where I should be happy if I had my dearest Emily, for I find already I cannot be happy without her; company, fine weather, prospect, good house and bed is nothing without my dear little wife is with me and enjoys it also. You tell me I don't know what you feel by (our) being so distant from each other – believe me I do, for I feel so much that it's impossible you can feel more, and shall never be happy till I am in those dear arms, which shall be (you may depend upon it) as soon as I can, without disobliging my friends here that expect to see me . . .

Correspondence of Emily, Duchess of Leinster 1731–1814, Dublin Stationery Office, 1949

Before automobiles brides were carried away from the church in whatever mode of transport was available. *Taking Home the Bride* by John Evan Hodgson.

designer, Lucile, Lady Duff Gordon, went to Brighton for her honeymoon where her husband hired the public baths for two days so that they might swim together in private. Those who could afford it travelled to Europe, to Paris or to Italy. These days Africa, Australia or even a trip around the world, if not common, is not unheard of.

There is no doubt that the married state in the past was considered to be a privileged one. Overnight, a young inconsequential couple became respected members of the community, heads of households who were given better pews in church than single people who would be required to defer to them. At christening feasts, for example, they were given better utensils than their unmarried friends. As a married couple they were required to show a wisdom in their actions that would not have been expected of them as unmarried people. The wealthy, too, were expected to assume new responsibilities as marriage often coincided with the inheritance of property, or a country seat – or perhaps several, which had to be managed and maintained. Family and friends did not concern themselves as to whether couples enjoyed each other's company: their interest lay more in waiting for news of the birth of the first child, preferably a male child, to secure the line of inheritance.

Literature and history have left us with touching examples of both happy and unhappy marriages, but what we cannot know is just how successful marriages were in the past, or, if the opportunity to divorce had been available to people, whether the divorce rate would have been any higher then than it is now. It is true that one's expectations of marriage as a practical and emotionally satisfying experience were likely to be far less than they are today, but that doesn't account for the human emotion of love which cannot be held within a marriage any more than it can be injected into a marriage. As for the future, perhaps these words, written by Dr Ernest R. Groves for the Duke Bar Association meeting on 24 April 1937 sum it up best:

Marriage is more secure today than any other human undertaking. It will outlive our present government and our contemporary church. Marriage is the most substantial of human relationships, but to make marriage successful, people must advance in their co-operation. They must adjust themselves to the changes in their ways of life and their effects on marriage. It is true that today we have more divorces, but it is also true that we have more marriages, and this means that our higher matrimonial program also brings liabilities. We may wish we could go back to the older, surer type of marriage, but that is impossible. Our solution must be preventative.

We are not nearly so busy as we should be in building up defenses which the new attack on marriage in modern life must bring.

IN little more than a month after that meeting on the hill – on a rainy morning in departing November – Adam and Dinah were married.

It was an event much thought of in the village. All Mr Burge's men had a holiday, and all Mr Poyser's; and most of those who had a holiday appeared in their best clothes at the wedding. I think there was hardly an inhabitant of Hayslope specially mentioned in this history and still resident in the parish on this November morning, who was not either in church to see Adam and Dinah married, or near the church door to greet them as they came forth. Mrs Irwine and her daughters were waiting at the churchyard gates in their carriage (for they had a carriage now) to shake hands with the bride and bridegroom, and wish them well; and in the absence of Miss Lydia Donnithorne at Bath, Mrs Best, Mr Mills, and Mr Craig had felt it incumbent on them to represent 'the family' at the Chase on the occasion. The churchyard walk was quite lined with familiar faces, many of them faces that had first looked at Dinah when she preached on the Green; and no wonder they showed this eager interest on her marriage morning, for nothing like Dinah and the history which had brought her and Adam Bede together had been known at Hayslope within the memory of man.

Bessy Cranage, in her neatest cap and frock, was crying, though she did not exactly know why; for, as her cousin Wiry Ben, who stood near her, judiciously suggested, Dinah was not going away, and if Bessy was in low spirits, the best thing for her to do was to follow Dinah's example, and marry an honest fellow who was ready to have her. Next to Bessy, just within the church door, there were the Poyser children, peeping round the corner of the pews to get a sight of the mysterious ceremony; Totty's face wearing an unusual air of anxiety at the idea of seeing Cousin Dinah come back looking rather old, for in Totty's experience no married people were young.

I envy them all the sight they had when the marriage was fairly ended and Adam led Dinah out of church. She was not in black this morning; for her aunt Poyser would by no means allow such a risk of incurring bad luck, and had herself made a present of the wedding dress, made all of grey, though in the usual Quaker form, for on this point Dinah could not give way. So the lily face looked out with sweet gravity from under a grey Quaker bonnet, neither smiling nor blushing, but with lips trembling a little under the weight of solemn feelings. Adam, as he pressed her arm to his side, walked with his old erectness and his head thrown rather backward as if to face all the world better; but it was not because he was particularly proud this morning, as is the wont of bridegrooms, for his happiness was of a kind that had little reference to men's opinion of it. There was a tinge of sadness in his deep joy; Dinah knew it, and did not feel aggrieved.

There were three other couples, following the bride and bridegroom: first, Martin Poyser, looking as cheery as a bright fire on this rimy morning, led quiet Mary Burge, the bridesmaid; then came Seth, serenely happy, with Mrs Poyser on his arm; and last of all Bartle Massey, with Lisbeth – Lisbeth in a new gown and bonnet, too busy with her pride in her son, and her delight in possessing the one daughter she had desired, to devise a single pretext for complaint.

Bartle Massey had consented to attend the wedding at Adam's earnest request, under protest against marriage in general, and the marriage of a sensible man in particular. Nevertheless, Mr Poyser had a joke against him after the wedding dinner, to the effect that in the vestry he had given the bride one more kiss than was necessary.

Behind this last couple came Mr Irwine, glad at heart over this good morning's work of joining Adam and Dinah. For he had seen Adam in the worst moments of his sorrow; and what better harvest from that painful seed-time could there be than this? The love that had brought hope and comfort in the hour of despair, the love that had found its way to the dark prison cell and to poor Hetty's darker soul – this strong, gentle love was to be Adam's companion and helper till death.

There was much shaking of hands mingled with 'God bless you's,' and other good wishes to the four couples, at the churchyard gate, Mr Poyser answering for the rest with unwonted vivacity of tongue, for he had all the appropriate wedding-day jokes at his command. And the women, he observed, could never do anything but put finger in eye at a wedding. Even Mrs Poyser could not trust herself to speak as the neighbours shook hands with her; and Lisbeth began to cry in the face of the very first person who told her she was getting young again.

Mr Joshua Rann, having a slight touch of rheumatism, did not join in the ringing of the bells this morning, and, looking on with some contempt at these informal greetings which required no official co-operation from the clerk, began to hum in his musical bass, 'Oh what a joyful thing it is,' by way of preluding a little to the effect he intended to produce in the wedding psalm next Sunday.

'That's a bit of good news to cheer Arthur,' said Mr Irwine to his mother, as they drove off. 'I shall write to him the first thing when we get home.'

George Eliot, *Adam Bede*

'WELL, my dear,' he deliberately began, 'considering we never saw her before, she seems a very pretty sort of young lady; and I dare say she was very much pleased with you. She speaks a little too quick. A little quickness of voice there is which rather hurts the ear. But I believe I am nice; I do not like strange voices; and nobody speaks like you and poor Miss Taylor. However, she seems a very obliging, pretty-behaved young lady, and no doubt will make him a very good wife. Though I think he had better not have married. I made the best excuses I could for not having been able to wait on him and Mrs Elton on this happy occasion; I said that I hoped I *should* in the course of the summer. But I ought to have gone before. Not to wait upon a bride is very remiss. Ah! it shews what a sad invalid I am! But I do not like the corner into Vicarage-lane.'

'I dare say your apologies were accepted, sir. Mr Elton knows you.'

'Yes: but a young lady – a bride – I ought to have paid my respects to her if possible. It was being very deficient.'

'But, my dear papa, you are no friend to matrimony; and therefore why should you be so anxious to pay your respects to a *bride*? It ought to be no recommendation to *you*. It is encouraging people to marry if you make so much of them.'

'No, my dear, I never encouraged any body to marry, but I would always wish to pay every proper attention to a lady – and a bride, especially, is never to be neglected. More is avowedly due to *her*. A bride, you know, my dear, is always the first in company, let the others be who they may.'

'Well, papa, if this is not encouragement to marry, I do not know what is. And I should never have expected you to be lending your sanction to such vanity-baits for poor young ladies.'

'My dear, you do not understand me. This is a matter of mere common politeness and good-breeding, and has nothing to do with any encouragement to people to marry.'

Jane Austen, *Emma*

THE wife can be no ways happy unless she be governed by a prudent lord, whose commands are sober counsels, whose authority is paternal, whose orders are provisions, and whose sentences are charity.

Jeremy Taylor, *The Marriage Ring*

WEDDING ANNIVERSARIES

Although sources vary slightly, most agree that the following list represents traditional wedding anniversary gifts. The most common anniversaries celebrated are at twenty-five years, forty years, fifty years and sixty years. In England the Queen sends a telegram to couples celebrating their diamond anniversaries.

1st - paper
2nd - cotton
3rd - leather
4th - fruit and flower or linen
5th - wood
6th - sugar and sweet or iron
7th - wool or copper
8th - bronze and rubber
9th - pottery and willow
10th - tin
11th - steel
12th - silk and fine linen

13th - lace
14th - ivory
15th - crystal
20th - china
25th - silver
30th - pearl or ivory
35th - coral
40th - ruby
45th - sapphire
50th - gold
55th - emerald
60th - diamond

Acknowledgements

The author and publisher are grateful to the following for permission to reproduce illustrations:

Bridgeman Art Library: *pages* 2–3, 22, 28, 32, 44, 48, 51, 57, 68, 89, 98, 118–9, 129, 145 (copyright The Tate Gallery, London), 156, 170; Hulton Picture Company: 15, 35, 91, 92, 176; The Mansell Collection: 8, 25, 31, 34, 90, 103, 116, 117, 121, 130, 154, 159, 165, 172, 180; Fine Art Photographic Library: 6, 79, 123, 149; Kurt E. Shon Ltd, New Orleans, Louisiana: 3, 10, 18–9, 23, 63, 115, 171, 179, 183; The Royal Collection, reproduced by gracious permission of Her Majesty the Queen: 4; Scala Instituto Fotografico Editoriale S.p.A./ the Galleria dell'Accademia, Florence: 26–7; Photographie Giraudon/Musée Condé: 16; Mary Evans Picture Library: 21, 74, 76, 84, 93, 139, 142, 147, 150; The Illustrated London News Picture Library: 24, 131, 143, 163, 168; British Museum: 29; Aberdeen Art Gallery and Museums, Aberdeen City Arts Department: 37 (below); Glasgow Art Gallery and Museum: 37 (above); Christie's New York: 49, 87, 133; MacConnal-Mason: 53, 94–5, 174–5; by courtesy of the Board of Trustees of the Victoria & Albert Museum: 58; Sotheby's London: 81, 126; private collection: 41; Walker Art Gallery, Liverpool: 52–3; Rifkin-Young Fine Arts Inc, New York: 166–7; Bibliothèque Nationale, Paris: 178, 187.

The quotations from *Marriage and Love in England (1300–1840)* by Alan Macfarlane are reproduced by permission of Basil Blackwell Ltd, New York; 'The Bells' by Edgar Allan Poe on page 159 is reprinted by permission of the publishers from *The Collected Works of Edgar Allan Poe*, Vol. 1, Thomas Ollive Mabbott, ed., Cambridge, Mass.: The Belknap Press of Harvard University Press, Copyright © 1969, The President and Fellows of Harvard College. The quotations from *The Ties That Bound* by Barbara A. Hanawalt and *For Better For Worse* by John R. Gillis are reproduced by permission of Oxford University Press, New York.

of Her Majesty during the wedding ceremonies. He was met at Windsor Station by Prince Henry of Battenberg, and, after lunching with the Queen, returned to Buckingham Palace for the remainder of his visit. The Crown Prince of Belgium, who represented the King and Queen of the Belgians at the wedding, arrived at Victoria on Tuesday morning, and was received by the Duke of Connaught and the Belgian Minister. By the same train General von Zeppelin, who represented the King of Wurtemberg, arrived in London, and drove off to the Grosvenor Hotel in one of the Royal carriages. Prince and Princess Henry of Prussia, the representatives of the German Emperor and Empress at the wedding, arrived at Queenborough on Wednesday morning, and were received at Victoria Station by the Duke of Connaught and Prince Christian. They immediately drove to Buckingham Palace, where they stayed during the week.

The Decorations in the Streets

IT seems as if every one, public authorities as well as private persons, had made an extra effort to brighten the streets of London for the Royal pageant. Beginning by St. James's Palace, where the ceremony took place, Pall Mall especially distinguished itself by its balconies, the Athenæum Club having a huge erection, and even Marlborough House having lofty stands behind the walls at the principal entrance. St. James's Street was a blaze of colour, and the houses in Piccadilly which look down the hill were draped with white and blue muslin, fringed with gold embroidery. But all up the slope from the Palace was a forest of masts crossed and intertwined with garlands of flowers; white flowers, ferns, and grasses were arranged round the masts at some distance from the ground.

The Wedding Morning

FROM an early hour on Thursday morning an enormous crowd thronged the streets. Indeed, it might have been part and parcel of the crowd which gave London its unwonted air the night previous. The last thing to be recollected of that day was the impression of strange thousands perambulating the tracks of omnibuses and running cabs out of their paths, and even those first afield on this morning found the throng still as great and continuous. In spite of the length of line to be kept, the regular troops on duty were not, perhaps, as numerous as on some former occasions, though the two events, the marriage procession and the subsequent departure, necessitated a double military programme. In all, some 7,000 troops were called into requisition, the route from Piccadilly to St. James's Park being kept respectively by detachments of the Grenadier, Coldstream, and Scots Guards, irrespective of Cavalry forming escorts, and having special positions assigned to them, and a strong force of Volunteers. In the afternoon, after a brief rest, the same troops were ready to re-form and keep the route to Liverpool Street.

The Programme of the Day

ABOUT eleven o'clock the invited guests arrived at the entrance to the Chapel, and were conducted to the seats reserved for them. At twenty minutes to twelve the Archbishop of Canterbury and the officiating clergy assembled in the Vestry of the Chapel Royal, and proceeded through the corridor of the Colour Chapel to the main entrance, while such other members of the Royal Family as took no part in the carriage processions were shown into their places by the ushers, among these being their Highnesses the Prince and Princess Edward of Saxe-Weimar, the Hereditary Prince of Hohenlohe, Count Mensdorff, and the Countesses Feodore, Victoria and Helena Gleichen. The first three carriages starting from Buckingham Palace to the Chapel were occupied by the

THE WEDDING BREAKFAST

Ladies and Gentlemen in Waiting. In the fourth arrived His Royal Highness Prince Albert of Belgium, His Royal Highness Prince Waldemar of Denmark, His Serene Highness Prince Philip of Saxe-Coburg and Gotha, General Count von Zeppelin, representing His Majesty the King of Wurtemberg. In the fifth carriage, the Equerry in Waiting to His Royal Highness the Duke of Cambridge, His Royal Highness the Duke of Cambridge. In the sixth carriage, Her Imperial and Royal Highness the Duchess of Edinburgh, Her Royal Highness the Princess Victoria Melita of Edinburgh, Her Royal Highness the Princess Alexandra of Edinburgh, Her Royal Highness the Princess Beatrice of Edinburgh. In the seventh carriage, their Royal Highnesses the Prince and Princess Henry of Battenberg, Her Highness the Princess Victoria of Battenberg, His Highness the Prince Alexander of Battenberg. In the eighth carriage, Her Royal Highness the Princess Louise, Marchioness of Lorne, and the Marquess of Lorne, their Serene Highnesses the Prince and Princess Louis of Battenberg and Princess Alexandra of Battenberg. In the ninth carriage, their Royal Highnesses the Prince and Princess Christian of Schleswig-Holstein their Highnesses the Princess Victoria and the Prince Albert of Schleswig-Holstein. In the tenth carriage, their Royal Highnesses the Duke and Duchess of Connaught, Her Royal Highness the Princess Margaret, Her Royal Highness the Princess Victoria Patricia, and His Royal Highness the Prince Arthur of Connaught.